Welcome to the
500 CALORIE DIET
Complete meal planner

The 2 days a week diet is the biggest new weight loss trend to come along in years, and no wonder! Who wouldn't want to diet only two days a week and still lose weight?

If you've been following the plan, or are thinking of trying it for the first time, the 500 Calorie Diet Complete Meal Planner has all you need. Our food editor Felicity has selected 101 super low cal recipes designed to fill you up and taste delicious, so fast days don't have to be boring. We've also made sure there are plenty of single servings and food you can make ahead and freeze, plus easy on the go lunches and fast meal ideas for when time is tight.

Good luck with the diet!

Editor Charlotte Richards
Art Director Deborah Hughes
Food Editor Felicity Barnum-Bobb
Picture Editor Kate Hockenhull
Thanks to Nathalie Gimson, Jackie Gallagher, Lisa Collins, Catherine Francis, Sarah Prescott
CONTACT Blue Fin Building, 110 Southwark Street, London SE1 0SU **Tel** 020 3148 5000
Email 52_diet_tech_support@ipcmedia.com
Brought to you by the makers of Woman magazine.
Editor: Karen Livermore **Art Director:** Dale Walker.
Published by IPC Media.

YOUR SHAPE UP

It's one of the most popular and easiest diets around, which is why 5:2 is the perfect way to lose a stone before summer. Here's how...

HOW DOES IT WORK?

It's simple. Two days a week, you eat no more than 500 calories. The other five days, you eat normally. That's it!

HOW MUCH WEIGHT WILL I LOSE?

Around 1½lb a week – more if you have a lot of weight to lose. The diet will also have an effect on your metabolism. Early studies suggest that people who follow the 500 calorie diet lose more actual fat, rather than the combination of fat, water and lean tissue that you lose on other diets. The two days fasting also helps you to eat normally on other days without piling the pounds back on.

ARE THERE ANY OTHER BENEFITS?

Studies of this type of diet show that not only do people see improvements in their blood pressure and cholesterol levels, but also in insulin sensitivity. It's even believed that it can reduce your risk of getting various cancers, heart disease and Alzheimer's disease.

HOW LONG DO I FOLLOW THE PLAN FOR?

Until you've achieved the weight you're happy with. At this point, you can maintain your weight and keep seeing the health benefits by having a 500-calorie day once a week.

WHAT DO I DO?

✱ Two days a week, you should eat no more than 500 calories (600 for men).
✱ The other five days a week, you can eat as normal. You should be aiming for around 2,000 calories a day, but don't worry if you have a blowout, such as dinner and/or drinks, a couple of times a week. See page 91 for what you should eat to ensure you get a healthy, balanced intake of all the right nutrients.
✱ The other good thing about this diet is that your 500-calorie days will help to stabilise your insulin levels and hunger. You should find your appetite is smaller on normal days, so you won't have to work so hard to stay around the 2,000 calorie mark.
✱ If you're on medication or have any ongoing medical condition, consult your GP before starting this diet plan.

Photo Jumpfoto

BREAKFAST
* Egg-topped portobello mushroom
100 calories

LUNCH
* Marinated prawns
130 calories

SNACK
* Hartley's Jelly No Added Sugar **6 calories**

DINNER
* Lemony chicken with veg cous cous
242 calories

TOTAL: 478 CALORIES

SNACK
6 calories

BREAKFAST
100 calories

LUNCH
130 calories

DINNER
242 calories

Making it EASIER

The 500 calorie diet is a straight forward plan, but there are ways to make it even simpler...

5 WAYS TO GET THE BEST FROM THE DIET

1 Plan. Choose two days when your diary isn't full of work or social events. Then pick the meals and snacks you plan to eat each day from the meal planner. Email yourself a shopping list of the ingredients for your chosen recipes. Make sure you've bought everything you plan to eat, so there's no danger of buying little off plan extras.

2 Schedule. Eat meals when you know you will be hungriest. So if you don't feel hungry first thing, save breakfast until later. Or if you prefer, stick to two meals a day and add them in with extra ingredients or sides from the calorie list (page 94).

3 Eat lean proteins. Aim to get the majority of your calorie intake from chicken or eggs and vegetables (leafy green veg is best). These are good, filling foods with low calorie counts, so you'll be able to enjoy eating decent-sized portions.

4 Drink lots of fluid! Water, black coffee, black or green tea, herbal teas and diet drinks are all virtually calorie-free. They'll keep you feeling full, take the edge off any hunger pangs and help you to beat those, 'I'm bored so I'll eat something' urges that you get during the day.

5 Snack low-cal. If you still feel hungry between meals, try low-calorie snacks, such as fat-free yogurt, fruit or a few unsalted almonds or Brazil nuts, to take the edge off. See the snack list on page 84 for more suggestions of our favourite low-calorie snacks.

SNEAKY 500 CALORIE SECRETS

✱ Use as many herbs and spices as you can in your cooking. The more flavour your food has, the easier you'll find it to cut down on the calories.

✱ Experiment with boiling, poaching and steaming food, as these cooking methods require no fat. Steaming in particular is a great way to make sure food retains its nutrients.

✱ Try to use unpeeled fruit and veg whenever possible, as the fibre levels will be higher so you'll feel fuller.

✱ To stop ingredients sticking in the pan, use a little water rather than oil.

✱ Still need to fry something? Invest in a can of low-cal cooking spray to keep the calorie count low.

✱ Desperate for something sweet? Try sugar-free jelly, which contains an average of just 8 calories per portion; or a square of dark chocolate (70% cocoa solids), at around 25 calories.

✱ Vegetable stock is lower in calories than meat stock, so use it as a base for soups and stews.

✱ Stock up on a few packs of shirataki noodles (Zero Noodles is a good brand). They contain no carbs and around just

7 calories per portion, and they're great for bulking up a meal so it feels more substantial. Just be sure to rinse the noodles well first, and mix them into whatever sauce or spices you're cooking with, as they'll take on the flavour of whatever they're cooked in.

Who's eating the 500 calorie way?

Beyoncé, Jennifer Lopez and Christy Turlington are all said to be 500 calorie fans

Phillip Schofield is just one of the celebrities following the 5:2 diet a try. The This Morning presenter has lost 2 stone and says his energy levels have rocketed. 'For me this is very workable. I like the science behind it,' he revealed recently.

We've heard that presenter Nadia Sawalha has also given the diet a go. Beyoncé, Jennifer Lopez, Christy Turlington the cast of *Corrie* and Hugh Fearnley-Whittingstall have all reportedly tried it, too.

Phillip Schofield was on a fast day during a recording of *All Star Mr & Mrs*

BREAKFAST

It's the most important meal of the day, so don't go hungry...

100 calories & under

3 WAYS with PORRIDGE

PORRIDGE with MAPLE SYRUP

Serves 1

Ingredients
* 20g porridge oats
* 2tbsp skimmed milk
* 1tsp maple syrup

Method
1 Put the oats in a deep, microwave-safe bowl with 2tbsp water and the milk. Microwave on High for 1 min 30 secs until the liquid is absorbed.
2 Stir in the maple syrup to serve.

CALORIES
100

CINNAMON PORRIDGE

Serves 1

Ingredients
* 20g porridge oats
* 3tbsp skimmed milk
* Pinch of sweetener
* Pinch of ground cinnamon

Method
1 Put the porridge oats in a deep, microwave-safe bowl with 2tbsp water and the milk.
2 Microwave on High for 1 min 30 secs until the oats are tender and the liquid has been absorbed. Sprinkle with the sweetener and cinnamon to serve.

CALORIES
86

PORRIDGE with BERRIES

Serves 1

Ingredients
* 25g porridge oats
* 30g fruit such as blueberries, raspberries and blackberries

Method
1 Put the porridge oats in a deep, microwave-safe bowl with 75ml water.
2 Microwave on High for 1 min 30 secs until the oats are tender and the liquid absorbed.
3 Top with the berries to serve.

CALORIES
100

Smart tip

Look out for zero-calorie sweeteners to stir into your porridge if you have a sweet tooth. Making this for the family? Use milk instead of water for a richer flavour.

EGG WHITE OMELETTE

Serves 1

Ingredients

* 80g baby spinach leaves
* 80g mushrooms, sliced
* 3 egg whites
* Salt and ground black pepper

Method

1 Heat a small non-stick frying pan. Add the spinach and cook for 2 mins until wilted.

2 Remove the spinach from the pan, add the mushrooms and cook for 3 mins to soften.

3 Meanwhile, whisk the egg whites with 2tbsp cold water, salt and ground black pepper. Pour into the frying pan and sprinkle with the spinach. Cook for 4 mins until the omelette is firm.

Smart tip

Keep cals low by frying the omelette with a spray or two of low-cal cooking spray (one cal per spray). Take breakfast up to your 100 calorie limit with a little fresh fruit. See the calorie list on p86 for inspiration.

CALORIES 66

BAKED BEANS on TOAST

Smart tip

Cut cals further by making Melba toast at 20 cals per slice. Toast 1 slice of bread, then cut in half horizontally. Toast the cut side until golden. Slice into 4. Store leftovers in an airtight container for up to 4 days.

CALORIES 88

Serves 1

Ingredients

* 1 slice of diet bread
* 50g reduced-sugar baked beans in tomato sauce

Method

1 Toast the bread and top with warmed baked beans.

FRAGRANT GINGER GRAPEFRUIT

Serves 4

Ingredients

* 2 pink or yellow grapefruit
* Few pinches of ground ginger
* 3-4tbsp demerara or caster sugar

Method

1 Preheat the grill to hot. Halve the grapefruit and use a grapefruit knife to loosen the segments from the peel.
2 Place the grapefruit halves, cut-side up, on a baking sheet. Sprinkle with the ginger, then the sugar.
3 Place the grapefruit under the hot grill for 3 mins to warm through and caramelise the sugar.

Smart tip

Grapefruit has only 50 cals per half. It contains a flavonoid called naringenin, which is thought to help stabilise blood sugar and encourage the body to burn fat more effectively, so it's perfect for fast days.

CALORIES
75

SCRAMBLED EGG and KETCHUP

Serves 1

Ingredients

* 1 medium egg
* 1tbsp skimmed milk
* Salt and ground black pepper
* 1tsp chives, chopped
* 1tsp low sugar/salt ketchup

Method

1 Put the egg and milk in a non-stick pan and break up with a fork.
2 Place over a gentle heat and stir with a wooden spoon until the egg is just becoming firm. Take off the heat.
3 Season with salt and ground black pepper, and sprinkle with chives. Serve with tomato ketchup.

Smart tip

Make the washing up easier and cook in the microwave. Mix the egg and milk in a microwave-safe bowl. Cook on High for 30 secs, mix with a fork and cook for a further 30 secs-1 min until just firm.

CALORIES
95

3 WAYS with YOGURT

VANILLA YOGURT with JUMBO OATS

Serves 1

Ingredients
* 75g low-fat vanilla yogurt
* 2tsp jumbo oats

Method
Spoon the yogurt into a bowl and sprinkle with the jumbo oats.

CALORIES
100

MANGO YOGURT with PASSION FRUIT

Serves 1

Ingredients
* 100g low-fat mango yogurt
* Juice and seeds from ½ passion fruit

Method
Spoon the yogurt into a bowl.
Holding the passion fruit half over the bowl, scoop out the seeds and squeeze the juice over the yogurt.

CALORIES
95

STRAWBERRY and ALMOND YOGURT

Serves 1

Ingredients
* 75g low-fat strawberry yogurt
* 50g strawberries, sliced
* 4g toasted flaked almonds

Method
Spoon the yogurt into a bowl and top with the strawberries.
Sprinkle with the almonds.

CALORIES
96

Smart tip

Invest in a pair of digital scales to be very accurate when weighing out high-cal foods, such as almonds. Serving this to non-dieters? Sprinkle yogurt with some sweet granola.

EGG-TOPPED PORTOBELLO MUSHROOM

Serves 1

Ingredients

* ✱ 1 large portobello mushroom (around 75g)
* ✱ 4 sprays of low-cal cooking spray
* ✱ 1 medium egg
* ✱ 1 sprig of parsley
* ✱ Ground black pepper

Method

1 Preheat the grill to high. Put the mushroom on a non-stick baking tray and moisten with 2 sprays of low-cal cooking spray. Grill for 5 mins. Turn, add another spray of oil, and cook for a further 2 mins.
2 Meanwhile, heat a non-stick pan with 2 sprays of oil. Crack in the egg and fry for 4 mins, until firm.
3 Serve the fried egg on top of the mushroom. Top with a sprig of parsley and a grind of black pepper.

Smart tip

If you want to use more oil on the mushroom to make it moister, try poaching the egg in boiling water for 4 mins instead of frying it to stay within your calorie limit.

CALORIES

100

BACON and GRILLED TOMATOES

Smart tip

You can swap the streaky bacon for 1 rasher of back bacon, if you like. Trim off all visible fat and check it weighs only 20g.

CALORIES
76

Serves 1

Ingredients
* 1 large tomato
* 20g rasher of streaky bacon
* Salt and ground black pepper

Method
1 Preheat the grill to high. Cut the tomato in half horizontally.
2 Line a grill pan with a non-stick sheet. Place the tomato and bacon in the grill pan.
3 Grill the tomato and bacon for 6 mins, turning as needed, until the bacon is crispy and the tomato tender. Season with salt and ground black pepper to serve.

PANCAKE with LEMON and CINNAMON

Serves 4

Ingredients
* 50g plain flour
* 1 medium egg, lightly beaten
* 150ml milk
* 5 sprays low-cal cooking spray
* ½tsp demerara sugar
* 2tsp lemon juice
* Pinch of ground cinnamon

Method
1 Put the flour in a bowl, add the egg and milk and whisk to make a smooth batter.
2 Spray a 15cm non-stick pan with low-cal cooking spray and heat. Pour in just enough batter to thinly cover the base of the pan. Tilt to coat evenly.
3 Cook for 30 secs until the pancake is firm and golden on the underside. Use a palette knife to turn the pancake (or toss if you're feeling adventurous). Cook for another 30 secs until the underside is firm and golden.
4 Slide onto a plate and keep warm. Repeat with the remaining batter to make 4 pancakes (interleaf with greaseproof paper to stop them sticking together).
5 Serve with a sprinkling of sugar, a squeeze of lemon juice and a pinch of ground cinnamon.

CALORIES
97

CINNAMON TOAST

Serves 1

Ingredients

✳ 1 slice of white bread
✳ ½tsp ground cinnamon

Method

1 Lightly toast the bread until golden, but still nice and soft.
2 Sprinkle with the ground cinnamon and serve immediately.

Smart tip

If you're feeding kids or non-dieters, spread the toast with low-fat spread, sprinkle with the ground cinnamon and a pinch of brown sugar, and pop back under the grill to melt.

CALORIES

91

BOILED EGG with SOLDIERS

Serves 1

Ingredients

✳ 1 small egg
✳ ½ slice diet bread

Method

1 Place the egg in a pan of water and bring to the boil. Cook for 4-8 mins, depending on how firm you like your yolk (see tip, right).
2 Meanwhile, toast the bread until pale golden and slice into mini-soldiers to dip. Serve with the egg.

Smart tip

For a really runny yolk, boil the egg for 4 mins. If you like your egg soft but not runny, then boil it for 6 mins. Boil for 8 mins if you like your egg almost hard-boiled.

CALORIES

97

3 SPEEDY FRUIT SALADS

FLORIDA COCKTAIL

Serves 1

Ingredients
* 1 small orange
* Half a grapefruit

Method
1 Peel and segment the orange, and serve on top of the grapefruit half.

CALORIES
86

TROPICAL FRUIT SALAD

Serves 6

Ingredients
* 1 papaya
* 1 small pineapple
* 1 mango
* 3 kiwi fruit
* 2 oranges
* 2 passion fruit
* 2tbsp light muscovado sugar
* Juice and grated zest of 1 lime

Method
1 Peel, deseed/core and chop all the fruit except the lime, and mix together in a bowl.
2 Sprinkle with the sugar and the lime juice and zest.
3 Chill until ready to serve. Will store in the fridge for up to three days.

CALORIES
100

Smart tip

To test if the papaya and mango are ripe, gently press the skin – it should 'give' slightly. If the fruit is hard, it will be unripe, sharp and unpleasant to eat.

STRAWBERRY, WATERMELON and GRAPES

Serves 1

Ingredients
* 100g strawberries
* 100g watermelon
* 50g seedless grapes

Method
1 Hull and slice the strawberries. Cut the watermelon into cubes, and cut the grapes in half.
2 Put all the fruit in a bowl and mix to serve.

CALORIES
88

10 FAST BREAKFASTS

Start the day and boost your energy with these quick, low-cal options

1 BERRY SMOOTHIE
Put 60g summer berries (such as raspberries, strawberries and blueberries), 1tsp sugar, 2tbsp apple juice and 4tbsp low-fat raspberry yogurt in a blender and process until smooth.
91 calories

2 FRUIT YOGURT WITH OATS AND BLUEBERRIES
Top a 100g pot of 0% fat fruit yogurt with 2tsp jumbo oats and 30g blueberries.
100 calories

3 TOASTED MINI BAGEL HALF WITH CREAM CHEESE
Toast ½ mini bagel (25g). Spread with 1tbsp extra light cream cheese.
85 calories

4 CHOCOLATE MILKSHAKE
Blend 125ml skimmed milk with an 11g sachet of Options chocolate.
80 calories

5 MOCHA
Make an espresso and add an 11g sachet of Options chocolate. Top with 100ml frothed skimmed milk.
72 calories

100 calories & under

6 SPECIAL K BERRIES
Pour 100ml skimmed milk over 15g Special K Red Berries and top with 3 raspberries.
87 calories

7 LATTE
Froth up 200ml skimmed milk and pour over an espresso. Sprinkle with 1tsp low-calorie chocolate powder.
82 calories

8 ORANGE AND STRAWBERRIES
Peel and segment 1 orange. Serve with 3 strawberries.
65 calories

9 RYE RYVITA AND MARMITE
Spread 2 Rye Ryvitas with 2tsp Marmite.
77 calories

10 HOT CINNAMON BANANA
Slice a small banana into a bowl and sprinkle with a pinch of ground cinnamon. Microwave on High for 30 secs.
95 calories

LUNCH

Tuck into these delicious and healthy midday hunger-busters!

150 calories & under

GREEK SALAD

Smart tip

Swap the lettuce for raw white cabbage for extra crunch. This works particularly well if you are preparing it ahead.

CALORIES
137

Serves 1 Prep 10 mins

Ingredients
* 50g cucumber, halved and sliced
* 25g red onion, thinly sliced
* 1 tomato (90g), cut into wedges
* Salt and ground black pepper
* 3 Greek black olives in brine, drained
* 50g reduced fat feta, diced
* 3 cos lettuce leaves, torn
* 1tbsp low-fat French dressing

Method
1 Mix together the cucumber, red onion and tomato, and season generously with salt and ground black pepper.
2 Toss in the olives, diced feta and torn lettuce leaves. Combine with the French dressing, to serve.

TUNA SALSA WRAP

Serves 1 Prep 5 mins

Ingredients
* 35g tuna in brine, drained
* Ground black pepper
* 2tbsp tomato salsa
* ½ soft corn tortilla (30g)
* 25g iceberg lettuce, shredded
* 50g cucumber, cut into matchsticks

Method
1 Put the tuna in a bowl, season with ground black pepper and stir in 1tbsp of the tomato salsa.
2 Place the corn tortilla on a sheet of greaseproof paper or foil, then spread with the tuna mixture. Sprinkle the shredded lettuce and cucumber matchsticks over the tuna.
3 Roll up tightly in the paper or foil, twisting the ends to secure. Serve the remaining salsa alongside.

Smart tip

Add all the salsa to the tuna mixture if you like, especially if you're serving it at once. We've only added half to the filling to stop the wrap going soggy when preparing it ahead.

CALORIES
150

SPICY SAAG ALOO

Serves 5 Prep 10 mins Cook 25 mins

Ingredients

* 2tbsp vegetable oil
* 1 onion, peeled and sliced
* 1 clove of garlic
* 1 red chilli, deseeded and sliced
* 1tbsp freshly grated ginger
* 1tsp (level) black mustard seeds
* 1tsp (level) cumin seeds
* 1tsp (level) turmeric
* 500g potatoes, scrubbed and cut into bite-sized chunks
* 250g spinach leaves, washed
* Salt

Method

1 Heat the oil in a pan, add the onion and cook for 4-5 mins over a medium heat until it starts to soften. Add the garlic, chilli, ginger and spices, and cook for 1 min.

2 Add the potato chunks to the pan and cook for 10-15 mins, stirring occasionally, until tender.

3 Add the spinach and stir until it wilts. Season to taste with salt.

Smart tip

This makes a filling spicy vegetarian dish. It keeps well in the fridge for up to three days and can be microwaved, so it's perfect if you want a quick, flavoursome lunch.

CALORIES

132

ROASTED VEG and COUS COUS SALAD

Serves 4 Prep 10 mins Cook 25 mins

Ingredients

* 1 red and 1 yellow pepper, deseeded and cut into wedges
* 1 red onion, cut into wedges
* 2 garlic cloves, chopped
* 2tbsp olive oil
* 75g giant couscous
* 250ml hot vegetable stock
* 180g sweetfire beetroot wedges with fiery sweet chilli marinade
* 100g rocket

Method

1 Heat the oven to 200°C, Gas 6. Put the peppers, onion and garlic in a roasting tin and drizzle with 1tbsp olive oil. Roast for 20 mins until the vegetables are tender.

2 Heat the remaining 1tbsp olive oil in a frying pan, add the couscous and fry for 3 mins, then pour in the vegetable stock. Simmer, stirring occasionally, for 15 mins until the liquid is absorbed and the couscous is plumped up and tender.

3 Mix in the roasted vegetables and divide between plates. Top with the beetroot wedges and a handful of rocket. Serve warm or cold.

CALORIES
150

BUTTERNUT SQUASH and CARROT SOUP

Serves 6 Prep 15 mins Cook 30 mins

Ingredients

* 1tsp sunflower oil
* 2 onions, chopped
* 5cm piece root ginger, peeled and finely chopped
* 2 garlic cloves, chopped
* 2tsp ground cumin
* 500g carrots, chopped
* 500g butternut squash, peeled, deseeded and chopped
* 1.5ltr vegetable stock
* 4tbsp coriander, chopped
* 6tsp 0% Greek yogurt

Method

1 Heat the oil in a saucepan. Add the onions, ginger, garlic and 1tbsp water, and cook gently for 5 mins, until soft.
2 Add the ground cumin and cook for 1 min, then add the carrots, butternut squash and vegetable stock. Bring to the boil, reduce to a simmer and cook for 20-25 mins, until the vegetables are soft.
3 Purée the soup in a blender until smooth. Stir in the chopped coriander and serve topped with a spoonful of Greek yogurt.

CALORIES
91

ZESTY CRAB

Serves 2 Prep 10 mins

Ingredients

* 100g white crabmeat
* Ground black pepper
* 2 spring onions, chopped
* 1tbsp chopped dill
* Finely grated zest of ½ lemon, and 1tsp lemon juice
* 100ml 0% Greek yogurt
* ½tsp salmon caviar
* 2 dill sprigs (optional)
* 1 slice of diet bread, toasted

Method

1 Put the crabmeat in a bowl and season with black pepper. Mix in the spring onions, dill, lemon zest and juice.
2 Put into 2 ramekins, press down firmly and top with the Greek yogurt. Top with the salmon caviar and dill sprigs, if using.
3 Toast the bread, cut into soldiers and serve with the crab.

Smart tip

Want to serve this as a posh snack for a friend? Pop a couple of poaching rings on a tray lined with baking parchment. Fill with the crab mixture. Top with yogurt and chill for 2 hrs before removing the rings.

CALORIES

121

PEA and HAM SOUP

Smart tip

This soup is great to make if you've boiled a gammon joint, because it makes the most of the cooking liquor. Chicken or vegetable stock is fine to use instead, though.

CALORIES
150

Serves 4 Prep 10 mins Cook 10 mins

Ingredients
* 1ltr ham stock
* 2 leftover cooked onions, roughly chopped
* 2 leftover cooked carrots, roughly chopped
* 300g frozen peas
* 100g cooked ham, cut into small chunks

Method
1 Put the ham stock in a large pan. Add the onions, carrots and peas. Bring to the boil and simmer for 10 mins, or until the peas are tender.
2 Use a stick blender or food processor to blend everything together until smooth. Add the ham chunks and warm through to serve.

FAST FISHBURGER

Serves 3 Prep 10 mins Cook 6 mins

Ingredients
* 400g white fish fillet, skinned
* 5tbsp chopped fresh parsley
* 1tbsp (rounded) capers, rinsed
* Grated zest of 1 large lemon
* Salt and ground black pepper
* 1tbsp olive oil
* Flour, for sprinkling
* 3 lettuce leaves
* 6 slices of cucumber

Method
1 Finely chop the fish. Mix in the parsley, capers and lemon zest, and season with salt and ground black pepper. Squeeze the mixture between your hands to drain out any liquid, then shape into 3 burgers. Chill for 20 mins.
2 Heat the oil in a pan. Sprinkle the flour on the burgers. Cook for 3 mins on each side, until golden and just cooked. Serve with the lettuce and cucumber.

Smart tip

For a great weekend lunch for non-dieters, serve the fishcake in a toasted bap, piled onto salad and topped with tartare sauce.

CALORIES
141

MANCHEGO and CHORIZO QUESADILLAS

Serves 4 Prep 5 mins Cook 5 mins

Ingredients

* Oil, for greasing
* 2 flour tortillas
* 35g Manchego cheese, grated
* 35g chorizo sausage, chopped
* 1tbsp chopped fresh coriander

Method

1 Heat a lightly oiled frying pan and lay a flour tortilla on it. Sprinkle with half the grated cheese. Scatter over the chorizo and coriander. Sprinkle with the remaining cheese and place the other flour tortilla on top.

2 Cook over a medium heat, pressing the top tortilla down well. Cook for 2-3 mins, until the bottom tortilla is golden and the cheese is starting to melt. Turn it over and cook on the other side for a further 2-3 mins.

3 Take off the heat. Cut the toasted quesadilla into 8 wedges, and serve 2 wedges per portion.

Smart tip

Want to take one to work with you? Cook lightly on one side until the cheese has just melted and the tortilla is barely toasted on one side (no need to flip and brown the other side). Make up to 150 cals with a green salad.

CALORIES

146

MARINATED PRAWNS

Serves 1 Prep 10 mins

Ingredients

* 5 large Madagascan prawns
* 1tsp capers, drained
* ¼ fennel, finely sliced
* 1 small shallot, finely chopped
* ¼ red chilli, deseeded and chopped
* ⅛ cucumber, halved and sliced
* 1tbsp white wine vinegar
* 1tsp olive oil

Method

1 Put the prawns in a large, shallow container. Add the capers, fennel, shallot, chilli and cucumber.
2 Drizzle with the vinegar and olive oil. Stir to coat, then cover and chill for at least 1 hr or overnight.

Smart tip

This prawn salad will also work well with regular small fresh or frozen prawns. Weigh out 50g to stay within your calorie allowance.

CALORIES

130

CARROT and LENTIL SOUP

Serves 2 Prep 15 mins Cook 25 mins

Ingredients

* 150g carrots, scrubbed and chopped
* 25g red split lentils
* 500ml hot vegetable stock
* ½tsp ground coriander
* Salt and ground black pepper

Method

1 Put the carrots in a pan with the lentils, vegetable stock and ground coriander. Season with salt and ground black pepper.
2 Bring to the boil and simmer for 25 mins, or until the carrots are tender. Pour into a food processor and blend until smooth. Warm through to serve.

Smart tip

For non-diet days, top the soup with a spoonful of soured cream. Add a sprinkling of crushed coriander seeds and some more ground black pepper, if you like.

CALORIES

80

ENGLISH GARDEN SALAD

Serves 4 Prep 10 mins

Ingredients

* 1 cucumber
* 2 cos (romaine) lettuces
* 8 radishes, halved
* A handful of small mint leaves, torn
* 1½tbsp olive oil
* Juice of 1 lemon
* Salt and ground black pepper
* 4 mini wholemeal rolls (40g each)

Method

1 Cut the cucumber into long wedges. Quarter each lettuce and arrange on plates with the cucumber, radishes and torn mint leaves.
2 Drizzle with the olive oil and lemon juice. Season with salt and ground black pepper, and serve with a mini roll.

Smart tip

A great lunchbox meal if you're avoiding carbs during the day. Try serving it with ½ hardboiled egg (37 cals) instead of the roll.

CALORIES

149

SOYA BEAN, PEA and SPINACH SOUP

Smart tip

If you don't have any spinach leaves, try using rocket or watercress instead. Fresh parsley, chives or coriander also work well instead of basil leaves, if that's what you've got in the fridge.

CALORIES

150

Serves 2 Prep 10 mins Cook 20 mins

Ingredients

* 75g frozen soya beans
* 125g frozen peas
* 300ml hot vegetable stock
* 3 spring onions, chopped
* A handful of fresh basil leaves
* 30g baby spinach leaves
* 150ml soya milk or skimmed milk
* Salt and ground black pepper

Method

1 Put the beans and peas in a pan with the stock. Add the spring onions, 2 basil leaves and the spinach. Bring to the boil and simmer for 10 mins.

2 Blend half the soup. Return to the pan with the milk and warm through. Season with salt and ground black pepper, and top with more basil leaves to serve.

KORMA CHICKEN DRUMSTICKS

Serves 2 Prep 5 mins Cook 35 mins

Ingredients

* Salt
* 2 skinless chicken drumsticks
* A pinch of poultry seasoning (we like Bart)
* 1 shallot, finely grated
* 1 small garlic clove, crushed
* 1tsp lemon juice
* 1½tbsp korma paste
* 4tsp low-fat natural yogurt
* 1tsp chopped fresh coriander
* 5 sprays low-cal cooking spray

Method

1 Dip your fingers in salt and pull the skin away from the chicken. Put the drumsticks in a shallow dish.

2 Cut a few slits in the drumsticks, and sprinkle with the poultry seasoning, grated shallot, garlic and lemon juice.

3 In a small bowl, mix together the korma paste, yogurt and coriander. Smother the mixture over the chicken, turning until well coated. Cover, chill and marinate for at least 30 mins.

4 Heat the oven to 200°C, Gas 6. Line a roasting tin with foil or a non-stick Teflon sheet. Lift the chicken out of the marinade, spray with low-cal cooking spray and cook in the oven for 35 mins, or until cooked through.

CALORIES

145

JALFREZI CURRY

Serves 8 Prep 20 mins Cook 40 mins

Ingredients

* 1tbsp sunflower oil
* 1 red onions, chopped
* 2 garlic cloves, crushed
* 1cm root ginger, grated
* 2 chillies, deseeded and chopped
* 450g jalfrezi sauce
* 400g can of chopped tomatoes
* 650g butternut squash, chopped
* 1 cauliflower, broken into florets
* Salt and ground black pepper
* 200g frozen peas
* 2tbsp coriander leaves

Method

1 Heat the oil in a large flameproof casserole. Fry the onions for 5 mins, to soften. Add the garlic, ginger and chillies, and cook for 1 min.

2 Pour in the jalfrezi sauce and the can of chopped tomatoes. Fill the can with water and add to the casserole.

3 Add the butternut squash and cauliflower. Season with salt and ground black pepper, and stir well. Cover and simmer gently for 30 mins, until the vegetables are tender.

4 Stir in the frozen peas and cook for a further 2 mins. Scatter with coriander leaves to serve.

Smart tip

Research suggests that chilli speeds up metabolism, so add extra chilli powder to meals for a quick fat-burning boost. Non-dieters can enjoy this curry with a toasted naan.

CALORIES 150

BUTTER BEAN STEW

Serves 4 Prep 5 mins Cook 20 mins

Ingredients

* ✱ 150g red onions, sliced
* ✱ 250g Mediterranean vegetables, cut into chunks
* ✱ 350g cherry tomato and basil sauce (we like Sacla')
* ✱ 400g can of butter beans, drained
* ✱ Handful of fresh basil leaves, optional

Method

1 Put the onions in a non-stick pan with 1tbsp water. Cook gently for 5 mins to soften.
2 Add the chunky vegetables and fry for 10 mins to soften.
3 Add the tomato and basil sauce and the butter beans, and warm through for 5 mins. Serve sprinkled with fresh basil leaves, if liked.

Smart tip

Look out for packs of ready-to-roast vegetables (onions, courgettes, peppers, tomatoes), available fresh or frozen.

CALORIES

149

BAKED SWEET POTATO

Smart tip

Want to make this in a rush? Place the sweet potato on a microwave-safe plate and microwave for 10 mins. Microwave the red pepper and garlic for 3 mins.

CALORIES

122

Serves 1 Prep 5 mins Cook 30 mins

Ingredients

* 100g sweet potato, scrubbed
* 75g red pepper, deseeded and chopped
* 1 garlic clove, crushed
* 20g 0% Greek yogurt
* Ground black pepper

Method

1 Preheat the oven to 220°C, Gas 7. Prick the skin of the sweet potato with a fork, and place in a roasting tin with the pepper and garlic. Bake in the oven for 30 mins, until tender.
2 Cut the potato in half and open. Spoon in the Greek yogurt, season with ground black pepper, and top with the roasted pepper.

SPICY TUNA and SALSA

Serves 2 Prep 15 mins Cook 2 mins

Ingredients

* 1tsp fresh ginger, finely grated
* 1 clove garlic, peeled and grated
* ½tsp ground coriander
* ¼tsp ground turmeric
* Pinch of cayenne pepper
* Salt and ground black pepper
* 2tsp sunflower oil
* 2 tuna steaks (50g each)
* Fresh coriander leaves
* Lime halves, to garnish
* 4tbsp low-fat natural yogurt
* 2 popadoms

For the chutney:

* ½ green chilli, deseeded and chopped
* Handful of mint leaves, washed
* 2tbsp fresh tomato salsa

Method

1 Mix the grated ginger, garlic, spices, seasoning and 2tsp of the sunflower oil in a shallow dish. Cut each tuna steak into 4 or 5 triangular pieces, and coat in the marinade. Leave for 10 mins to marinate.
2 To make the chutney, stir the chilli and mint leaves into the fresh tomato salsa. Put in a serving bowl.
3 Heat a frying pan and, when piping hot, add the remaining 1tsp sunflower oil and fry the tuna for 1 min on each side, or until cooked through.
4 Scatter with fresh coriander leaves and garnish with the lime halves. Serve with the tomato and mint chutney, yogurt and popadoms on the side.

CALORIES

148

PRAWN SALAD with PICKLED CUCUMBER

Serves 4 Prep 25 mins Cook 5 mins

Ingredients

* 1 cucumber
* Sea salt and ground black pepper
* 4 handfuls of baby spinach leaves
* 3tsp sesame oil
* 280g raw tiger prawns

For the dressing:

* 1 clove of garlic, peeled and very finely chopped
* ½ small red chilli, deseeded and very finely chopped
* 1tsp brown sugar
* 1tbsp fish sauce
* 4tbsp lime juice
* 3tsp sesame oil
* 2tbsp freshly chopped coriander

Method

1 Peel the cucumber and cut into fine slices on the diagonal. Put in a colander and sprinkle with 2tsp sea salt. Leave for 1hr, if possible, to extract the water.
2 To make the dressing, whisk all the ingredients in a large bowl. Rinse the cucumber under cold water and pat dry with a tea towel. Add to the dressing and stir in gently. Season with ground black pepper. Put the spinach leaves in 4 bowls and spoon the cucumber on top.
3 Heat 1tsp of the sesame oil in a pan. Cook the prawns for 3 mins until they turn pink. Spoon onto the salad and add any leftover dressing. Sprinkle with the remaining oil and coriander to serve.

CALORIES
123

FIVE VEG STIR-FRY

Serves 4 Prep 15 mins Cook 5 mins

Ingredients

* 1tbsp olive oil
* 1 carrot, cut into matchsticks
* 100g asparagus, tips cut off and reserved, stalks halved lengthways
* 100g Tenderstem broccoli
* 100g runner beans, sliced
* 100g sugar snap peas
* 4tbsp balsamic vinegar
* Handful of chopped fresh parsley
* Salt and ground black pepper

Method

1 Heat the oil in a large wok, and stir-fry the carrot for 1 min. Add the asparagus stalks, broccoli and runner beans, and stir-fry for 1 min. Add the asparagus tips and sugar snap peas. Stir-fry for 2 mins.
2 Stir in the balsamic vinegar. Sprinkle with parsley. Season to taste with salt and ground black pepper to serve.

Smart tip

This can be adapted as a healthy lunch for the kids, too. Cook 2 blocks of medium egg noodles in boiling salted water for 4 mins. Drain and toss into the vegetables with a splash of low-fat dressing.

CALORIES
80

SQUASH and VEGETABLE TAGINE

Serves 4   Prep 5 mins   Cook 4-8 hrs

Ingredients

* 2tsp sunflower oil
* 1 large onion, cut into thin wedges
* 400g butternut squash, peeled, deseeded and cut into chunks
* 3 parsnips, peeled and cut into chunks
* 300g cauliflower, broken into florets
* 100g carrots, peeled and sliced
* 100g red pepper, deseeded and chopped
* 1tbsp (level) ground coriander
* 1tbsp (level) ground cumin
* 1tbsp (level) ground turmeric
* 400g can of chopped tomatoes
* 1 vegetable stock cube
* 100g chickpeas, drained and rinsed
* Salt and ground black pepper
* 2tbsp chopped fresh coriander

Method

1 Heat the sunflower oil in a large pan. Add the onion wedges and cook for 5 mins, until starting to soften. Add all the other vegetables and cook for a further 5 mins, stirring occasionally, until softened.

2 Add the ground coriander, cumin and turmeric, and cook for a further 2 mins. Stir in the chopped tomatoes and 300ml water. Crumble in the stock cube and bring to the boil. Stir in the chickpeas and season well with salt and ground black pepper.

3 Pour the mixture into the bowl of a slow cooker, and set to cook on high for 3-4 hrs, or on low for 7-8 hrs, until the vegetables are tender. Sprinkle with chopped coriander to serve.

Smart tip

This tagine freezes well. Line foil containers with plastic bags, fill with the tagine, seal and freeze. To serve, put in a bowl and microwave for 5 mins per portion, until defrosted and warmed through.

CALORIES
150

TABBOULEH

Serves 1 Prep 5 mins Cook 15 mins

Ingredients
* 25g bulgur wheat
* 2tsp lemon juice
* Salt and ground black pepper
* 1 Little Gem lettuce, shredded
* 50g cucumber, finely chopped
* 1tbsp chopped fresh parsley
* 1tbsp torn mint leaves
* 30g reduced fat feta, crumbled

Method
1 Cook the bulgur wheat in boiling salted water for 15 mins, until tender. Drain and rinse in cold water.
2 Put the wheat in a large bowl. Add the lemon juice and season with salt and ground black pepper.
3 Add the lettuce, cucumber, parsley, mint and feta, and gently stir in.

Smart tip

You can swap the lettuce for 1 small ripe tomato, if you like. Finely chop the tomato and combine with the other ingredients.

CALORIES
148

FIERY PRAWN TOM YAM SOUP

Serves 4 Prep 10 mins Cook 15 mins

Ingredients

* 1.4ltr vegetable or chicken stock
* 3tsp tom yam paste
* 2 lemongrass stalks, halved
* 5 dried lime leaves (we used Bart)
* 400g sweet potatoes, cubed
* Juice of 2 limes
* 12 button mushrooms, halved
* 1 red chilli, deseeded and sliced
* 200g raw prawns
* Small bunch of coriander leaves

Method

1 Put the stock and tom yam paste in a large pan. Stir in the lemongrass, lime leaves and sweet potatoes. Bring to the boil and simmer for 10 mins.

2 Add the lime juice, mushrooms, red chilli and prawns. Simmer for 3 mins until the prawns turn pink. Scatter with coriander leaves to serve.

Smart tip

Leftover roast pork, beef or chicken? You can use that instead of prawns, if you like. Remember to remove all traces of fat, so it's lean.

CALORIES
150

ASPARAGUS with LEMON CRUMB

Serves 3 Prep 10 mins Cook 6 mins

Ingredients

* 500g asparagus spears, rinsed and dried
* 2tbsp olive oil
* 1 lemon
* 50g day-old bread, made into crumbs
* 1 clove of garlic, peeled and grated
* 1tbsp chopped fresh parsley
* Sea salt and ground black pepper

Method

1 Heat a griddle pan. Coat the asparagus spears in half the olive oil and griddle in batches over a medium heat until tender. Set aside, keeping it warm. Pare the zest from half the lemon in long, thin strips.

2 Heat the rest of the olive oil in a frying pan. Add the breadcrumbs and grated garlic, and stir over a medium heat until golden. Remove from the heat and stir in the lemon zest and chopped fresh parsley. Season generously with salt and ground black pepper.

3 Cut the lemon into wedges and brown on the griddle.

4 Arrange the asparagus on warmed plates and spoon the crumb mixture over the top. Serve with the griddled lemon wedges for squeezing over.

CALORIES
147

ORIENTAL SOYA BEAN SALAD

Smart tip

You'll find soya beans in the supermarket, next to the frozen peas. They're a great veggie source of protein, so this salad is nice and filling. Have a satsuma for afters – just 26 cals.

CALORIES 131

Serves 1 Prep 10 mins Cook 6 mins

Ingredients

* 75g frozen soya beans
* Salt and ground black pepper
* 1tsp soy sauce
* 2tsp rice vinegar
* 1tsp lemon juice
* 50g cucumber
* 1 spring onion, trimmed
* 50g radishes, trimmed

Method

1 Cook the soya beans in boiling salted water for 6 mins until tender. Drain.
2 Put the soya beans in a bowl. Season with salt and ground black pepper. Add the soy sauce, vinegar and lemon juice.
3 Chop the cucumber, spring onions and radishes, and stir into the soya beans.

CREAMY CRABSTICK LETTUCE WRAP

Serves 1 Prep 10 mins

Ingredients

* 25g low-fat cream cheese
* Salt and ground black pepper
* 1tsp sweet chilli sauce
* 1 large outer iceberg lettuce leaf
* 50g crabsticks
* 1 small carrot, cut into matchsticks
* 50g red pepper, cut into matchsticks
* 25g cucumber, cut into matchsticks

Method

1 Put the cream cheese in a bowl. Season with salt and ground black pepper, and stir in the sweet chilli sauce.
2 Place the lettuce leaf on greaseproof paper. Spread with the cream cheese. Scatter with the crabsticks and veg. Roll up, twisting the paper to secure.

Smart tip

This is best made when you've just bought a new iceberg lettuce, as you need to use the super-large outer leaf. Serve with ½tsp pickled ginger for extra kick.

CALORIES 116

WARM LEMON CHICKEN

Serves 6 Prep 20 mins Cook 15 mins

Ingredients

* 6 boneless chicken thighs
* Salt and ground black pepper
* 3 garlic cloves, crushed
* Zest and juice of 2 lemons
* 6 sprigs of fresh thyme
  (or 2tsp dried thyme)
* 5tsp olive oil
* 100g baby spinach leaves
* ½ red cabbage, shredded
* 4 carrots, cut into ribbons
* 1tbsp balsamic vinegar

Method

1 Pull the skin off the chicken thighs. Place 1 thigh between 2 sheets of baking parchment and hit with a rolling pin to flatten. Repeat with the other chicken thighs.

2 Put the chicken in a shallow dish, and season generously with salt and ground black pepper. Add the garlic, lemon zest and half the lemon juice. Sprinkle with the thyme.

3 Heat the olive oil in a griddle or heavy-based pan. Fry the chicken for 15 mins, turning, until golden and cooked through.

4 Mix together the spinach, red cabbage and carrots. Divide the salad between the plates and top with the chicken. Drizzle with the remaining lemon juice, balsamic vinegar and any cooking juices.

Smart tip

Have this for dinner instead of lunch and you can add 100 cals of veg for a really satisfying evening meal. Try 50g baby new potatoes (38 cals), plus 100g steamed broccoli (35 cals).

CALORIES

142

THAI VEGGIE SPRING ROLLS

Makes 6 Prep 15 mins

Ingredients

* 25g dried rice vermicelli noodles
* 1 carrot, cut into matchsticks
* ½ small cucumber, cut into matchsticks
* 1 red peppers, cut into matchsticks
* 1½ spring onions, thinly sliced
* 6 circular rice-paper discs
* 2tbsp mint leaves
* 2tbsp coriander leaves
* 1½tsp brown sugar
* 1tbsp lime juice
* 1tbsp Thai fish sauce
* ½ small red chilli, diced

Method

1 Put noodles in a bowl, cover with boiling water and leave for 5 mins.
2 Combine carrots, cucumber, red pepper and spring onions. Stir through the drained noodles.
3 Dip each rice-paper disc into a bowl of hot water for 10 secs until soft. Lay a disc on a board and place some noodle mix in the centre, top with mint and coriander leaves, fold in the edges and roll up. Repeat until all the discs and filling is used up.
4 To make the dipping sauce: mix the sugar, lime juice, fish sauce and chilli. Serve alongside the rolls.

Smart tip

To make this tasty lunch a vegetarian option, use a light soy sauce instead of the Thai fish sauce.

CALORIES

43

ORIENTAL CHICKEN CHILLI SALAD

Serves 4 Prep 10 mins Cook 7 mins

Ingredients

* 1tsp vegetable oil
* 375g skinless, boneless chicken thighs, diced
* 2tbsp lemongrass, finely sliced
* 2 small red chillies, finely sliced
* 1 small red onion, thinly sliced
* 3tbsp lime juice
* 3tbsp fish sauce
* 1tsp sesame oil
* 1 small cucumber, cut into sticks
* 1 carrot, cut into ribbons
* 2 Little Gem lettuce, leaves separated
* Handful mint leaves
* Handful coriander leaves
* 1 lime, quartered

Method

1 Heat oil in a non-stick wok and fry the chicken for 5 mins or until just cooked.
2 Add the lemongrass, chillies and onions and fry for 2 mins.
3 Remove from heat. Pour lime juice, fish sauce and sesame oil into a jar and shake to mix.
4 Stir together the cooked chicken, cucumber, carrot, lettuce, mint and coriander leaves. Drizzle over the dressing and serve with lime wedges.

CALORIES
145

SPICY LENTIL, CARROT AND TOMATO SOUP

Serves 4 Prep 15 mins Cook 25 mins

Ingredients

* 1 onion, finely diced
* 1tsp vegetable oil
* 500g carrots, scrubbed and chopped
* 60g red lentils
* 600ml hot vegetable stock
* 2 x 400g can tinned tomatoes
* 1tbsp tomato purée
* 2tsp ground coriander
* Salt and black pepper
* 4tbsp half-fat sour cream
* ½tsp coriander seeds, crushed
* 1 small bunch chives, chopped

Method

1 Gently fry the onion in the oil for 5 mins until softened.
2 Add carrots, lentils, stock, tomatoes, purée, ground coriander and seasoning. Bring to the boil, then simmer for 25 mins until the carrots are tender.
3 Pour the soup into a blender and whizz until smooth.
4 Serve in bowls and top each with 1tbsp of sour cream, a sprinkling of crushed coriander seeds and some chopped chives.

CALORIES
147

Smart tip

Experiment with other spices for a different flavour to this filling soup. Try using smoked paprika instead of coriander to get an authentic Spanish taste.

10 FAST LUNCHES

Need a quick bite? Try these satisfying low-cal dishes...

1 JACKET POTATO & VEG
Pierce a 125g potato. Microwave until soft. Microwave 50g broccoli with 50g sliced red pepper in 1tbsp water for 2 mins. Fill the potato with 1tbsp low-fat salad cream and the veg.

145 calories

2 CHICKPEA AND TOMATO SALAD
Mix 1 chopped tomato with 75g chickpeas, 1 chopped shallot, 1tbsp mint, 1tbsp parsley and 1tbsp low-fat dressing. Season to taste.

123 calories

3 ASIAN CRAB SALAD
Mix ¼ cucumber with 1 carrot, both cut into matchsticks, and 50g green salad leaves. Add 75g halved crab sticks. Mix 1tsp soy sauce, 1tsp lime juice and 2tsp low-fat French dressing, and drizzle over.

77 calories

4 CHICKEN TIKKA SALAD
Shred ⅛ iceberg lettuce. Top with ¼ sliced red pepper, ¼ cucumber, chopped, and 75g chicken tikka. Mix with 1tbsp low-fat dressing.

150 calories

5 SOYA BEANS
Mix 1tsp light soy sauce and 1tsp vinegar. Drizzle over 100g soya beans, cooked from frozen.

137 calories

150 calories & under

6 FRIED EGG ON BAKED BEANS
Use 1 spray of low-cal cooking spray to fry an egg. Serve on 50g baked beans in tomato sauce.

126 calories

7 GUACAMOLE AND PITTA
Serve 3tbsp low-fat guacamole with ½ cucumber, cut into matchsticks, and 1 mini pitta.

149 calories

8 MINI PITTA WITH HAM AND WATERCRESS
Toast 1 mini pitta. Split and fill with 1 slice of lean ham and 50g watercress.

107 calories

9 LOW-CAL CREAM CHEESE AND CUCUMBER SANDWICH
Make a sandwich with 2 slices of Weight Watchers white bread, spread with 2tbsp low-fat cream cheese and filled with 4 slices of cucumber.

148 calories

10 PRAWN SALAD
Break up 1 Little Gem lettuce. Top with 75g prawns and drizzle with 2tbsp low-fat thousand island dressing.

150 calories

Fancy a new 'do for summer?

DON'T MISS THE WOMAN STYLE SPECIAL!

On sale 8 May

OVER 50 IDEAS FOR EVERY CUT & COLOUR

PLUS! ANTI-AGEING BEAUTY SECRETS, NEW MAKE-UP TRENDS AND THE BEST NEW BAGS AND SHOES!

DINNER

Supper doesn't have to be boring with these low-cal feasts

250 calories & under

VEGGIE SPAGHETTI

Serves 4 Prep 5 mins Cook 10 mins

Ingredients

* Bag of 5 mixed sweet peppers (in a microwaveable plastic bag)
* 200g dried spaghetti
* 200g frozen leaf spinach
* 1tsp garlic purée or paste (such as Very Lazy)
* Salt and ground black pepper

Method

1 Pierce the bag of peppers a couple of times. Microwave on High for 5 mins.
2 Meanwhile, cook the spaghetti in boiling salted water for 10 mins until tender, but with a slight bite.
3 Put the spinach in a bowl with the garlic purée or paste and microwave on High for 3 mins. Tip into a sieve over a bowl and use a potato masher to squeeze all the excess water out of the spinach.
4 Carefully remove the peppers from the bag. Cut off the stalk ends and pull out the seeds. Slice the peppers.
5 Drain the spaghetti, add the spinach and peppers and toss together. Season generously with salt and ground black pepper and serve immediately.

Smart tip

No microwave? Roast the peppers in the oven at 200°C, Gas 6 for 30 mins until tender and beginning to char. Red, yellow and orange peppers tend to be sweeter than green, so are better for roasting.

CALORIES

240

Serves 4 Prep 10 mins Cook 12 mins

Ingredients

* 6tsp olive oil
* 2 sirloin steaks (150g each)
* Salt and ground black pepper
* 2 oranges: 1 juiced, 1 segmented
* 2tsp sherry vinegar
* 1tsp (rounded) Dijon mustard
* 1 red onion, cut into 8 wedges
* 2 heads of white chicory, each sliced into 4 pieces lengthways
* 1 head of red chicory, shredded
* A large handful of rocket leaves

Method

1 Heat a frying pan over a medium heat. Rub 1tsp oil over each steak, and season with salt and ground black pepper. Fry for 1½-2 mins on each side. Wrap in foil and set aside.

2 Put the orange juice in a small pan. Bring to the boil and bubble until syrupy and reduced by half. Take off the heat and whisk in the vinegar, mustard and 1tsp oil. Season to taste.

3 Toss the onion and chicory in the remaining oil. Griddle them for a few mins until browning and tender.

4 Slice the steaks thinly. Mix all the warm ingredients with the orange segments, red chicory and rocket. Toss in the orange dressing to serve.

Smart tip

Chicory has quite a bitter flavour, so it may not appeal to everyone. For something milder, try ¼ white cabbage and ⅛ red cabbage, both finely shredded.

CALORIES

179

SPEEDY CHICKEN DINNER

Serves 4 Prep 5 mins Cook 30 mins

Ingredients

* ✱ 6 chicken thighs
* ✱ Salt and ground black pepper
* ✱ 2tsp chicken seasoning
* ✱ 400g ready-to-roast Mediterranean vegetables (onions, courgettes, peppers, cherry tomatoes)
* ✱ 2 garlic cloves, crushed
* ✱ Juice of 2 lemons
* ✱ 2tbsp olive oil

Method

1 Preheat the oven to 200°C, Gas 6. Put the chicken thighs in a roasting tin and sprinkle with salt, ground black pepper and chicken seasoning.
2 Add the Mediterranean vegetables and crushed garlic. Squeeze over the lemon juice and drizzle with the olive oil.
3 Roast in the oven for 30 mins, until the chicken is golden.

Smart tip

Serve with a 75g jacket potato (cooked weight), but make sure you don't add any butter or margarine. Non-dieters can enjoy roast potatoes on the side.

CALORIES

177

TASTY FISH PARCELS

Smart tip

Save this meal for when you've been good in the day, because it's slightly higher in calories. Serve with boiled new potatoes for non-dieters.

Serves 2 Prep 10 mins Cook 15 mins

Ingredients

* 2 skinless cod or haddock fillets (160g each)
* 2tsp (level) horseradish sauce
* 100g button mushrooms, sliced
* 2 spring onions, sliced
* 100g raw tiger prawns, thawed if frozen
* Salt and ground black pepper
* Green beans, to serve

Method

Preheat the oven to 200°C, Gas 6. Place each fish fillet on a large square of baking parchment. If the fish is very long and thin, cut it in half and place one half on top of the other.

Spread horseradish sauce over the fillets, then top with the mushrooms and spring onions. Arrange the prawns in a line on top of each fillet, and season with salt and ground black pepper.

Wrap the baking parchment over the fish and fold it over several times along the top. Fold the ends up several times and tuck under the parcels, or twist tightly to secure them.

Place the parcels on a baking tray and bake in the centre of the oven for 15 mins, or until the fish is cooked. You should be able to see the prawns turn pink through the paper. Serve immediately with steamed green beans.

CALORIES

184

SIMPLE CHICKEN KORMA

Serves 4 Prep 5 mins Cook 30 mins

Ingredients

* 2tsp sunflower oil
* 1 onion, chopped
* 425g chicken fillets, sliced
* 100ml single cream
* 4tbsp Korma paste
* 2tsp flaked almonds, toasted

Method

1 Heat the oil in a frying pan. Add the onion and fry for 3 mins, until softened.
2 Add the chicken and stir-fry for 3 mins. Stir in the cream and Korma paste.
3 Cover and simmer for 20 mins, until the chicken is tender and the sauce has thickened.
4 Scatter with the toasted flaked almonds and serve immediately.

Smart tip

Rice is high in cals – 15g raw weight is 50 cals! Measure out carefully and put in a bowl with three times the amount of water. Microwave on High for 2 mins. Stand for 5 mins until the liquid is absorbed and the rice tender.

CALORIES

234

MEDITERRANEAN AUBERGINES

Serves 4 Prep 20 mins Cook 45 mins

Ingredients

* 3tbsp olive oil
* 1 onion, peeled and chopped
* 1-2 cloves of garlic
* 400g can of chopped tomatoes
* 1tbsp tomato ketchup
* Salt and ground black pepper
* 2 large aubergines
* 60g stoned olives, drained and chopped
* 60g mozzarella, grated
* 10 basil leaves, shredded

Method

1 Heat 1tbsp of the oil and fry the onion for 3 mins. Add the garlic and cook for a further 5 mins. Stir in the chopped tomatoes and ketchup and simmer, uncovered, for 10-15 mins, until thickened. Season with salt and ground black pepper.

2 Cut each aubergine into 8 thin slices. Pick out the largest 12 slices. Brush these on both sides with the oil, and griddle or grill in batches until browned. Set aside. Griddle or grill the rest of the aubergine slices, then chop them and put in a bowl.

3 Add the olives and 4tbsp of the tomato sauce mixture to the chopped aubergine, and mix well. Spoon half the remaining tomato sauce into the base of a baking dish.

4 Preheat the oven to 200°C, Gas 6. Lay the aubergine slices out on a board and divide the filling between them. Sprinkle with half the grated mozzarella and half the shredded basil leaves. Roll each slice up.

5 Pack the rolls in the dish, seam-side down. Spoon the remaining sauce over the top and sprinkle with the remaining mozzarella. Bake in the oven for 20 mins. Sprinkle with the rest of the shredded basil to serve.

CALORIES 180

MEXICAN CHICKEN FAJITAS

Serves 4 Prep 15 mins Cook 12 mins

Ingredients

* 2 x 200g skinless chicken breasts
* 1tbsp oil
* 1 garlic clove, peeled and crushed
* 35g pack of fajita seasoning mix
* 2 small peppers, 1 red, 1 green, deseeded and sliced
* 1 red onion, peeled and sliced
* 2 flour tortillas, warmed

Method

1 Coat the chicken breasts with a little of the oil and the crushed garlic, and sprinkle with the fajita seasoning mix.

2 Heat the remaining oil in a frying pan and cook the chicken on one side for 5 mins. Turn the chicken and add the sliced peppers and onion to the pan. Cook for a further 5 mins, or until the chicken is cooked through and the vegetables have softened.

3 Cut the chicken into slivers. Cut the flour tortillas in half. Fill the tortillas with the chicken, peppers and onions, and roll up.

Smart tip

Fajitas are traditionally served with extras on the side – but that's where the calories can pile on. So hold off on adding anything else to your wrap. Serve up tomato salsa and guacamole for non-dieters.

CALORIES

250

Dinner

Serves 4 Prep 10 mins Cook 20 mins

Ingredients

* ✱ 1tbsp olive oil
* ✱ 1 small onion, peeled and chopped
* ✱ 500g passata
* ✱ 150g can of cannellini beans, rinsed and drained
* ✱ 60g orzo pasta
* ✱ Large pinch of dried oregano
* ✱ 1 vegetable or chicken stock cube
* ✱ 125g cooked vegetables (eg carrots and parsnips), chopped
* ✱ 100g cooked meat (eg gammon), cut into small chunks
* ✱ A handful of cooked, shredded cabbage
* ✱ Salt and ground black pepper

Method

1 Heat the oil in a large pan and cook the onion for 5 mins until softened.
2 Add the passata and 500ml water. Add the cannellini beans, pasta and oregano. Crumble in the stock cube.
3 Bring the mixture to the boil and simmer for 10 mins. Add the cooked vegetables and meat. Heat through.
4 Meanwhile, heat the cooked cabbage in the microwave. Season the soup with salt and ground black pepper. Serve topped with the cabbage.

Smart tip

This is a perfect recipe to use up leftover vegetables and meat from Sunday lunch – lean chicken, beef, lamb, pork or gammon will all work well. Just make sure to remove all visible fat.

CALORIES

200

MEDITERRANEAN VEGGIE CHILLI

Serves 6 Prep 10 mins Cook 30 mins

Ingredients

* 3tbsp olive oil
* 2 red onions, diced
* 3 mixed peppers, deseeded and diced
* 2 courgettes, diced
* 1 large aubergine, diced
* 4-6tsp Cajun spice mix (depending on how spicy you like it)
* 2 x 400g tins of cherry tomatoes in juice
* 400g tin of kidney beans, drained
* 250g spinach leaves

Method

1 Put the olive oil, onions, peppers, courgettes, aubergine and Cajun spice mix in a large saucepan. Cook over a medium heat for 10 mins.
2 Add the tinned tomatoes and kidney beans, and simmer for a further 15 mins. Stir in the spinach leaves to wilt.

Smart tip

Family to feed? Toast 20cm flour tortillas (94 cals each) until golden, then cut into triangles. Serve with low-fat guacamole and natural yogurt for non-dieters.

CALORIES

203

ZESTY PORK SKEWERS

Serves 6 Prep 15 mins Cook 10 mins

Ingredients

* 3tbsp olive oil
* Zest and juice of 1 lemon
* 2 garlic cloves, crushed
* ½tsp ground ginger
* 1tsp ground coriander
* 2tbsp parsley, chopped
* 500g pork fillet, cut into bite-sized chunks
* Salt and ground black pepper
* Lemon wedges or chargrilled nectarines wrapped in Parma ham, to serve

Method

1 In a shallow dish, whisk together the oil, lemon zest and juice, garlic, ginger, coriander and parsley.

2 Add the pork chunks and season generously with salt and ground black pepper. Stir to evenly coat the pork in the marinade.

3 Preheat the grill or barbecue until hot. Take 18 mini skewers (soak wooden skewers first, to stop them burning) and thread 3 pieces of meat onto each one.

4 Cook the skewers on the grill or barbecue for 10 mins, turning occasionally, until lightly charred and cooked through. Serve with the lemon wedges or chargrilled nectarines wrapped in Parma ham.

CALORIES

156

CRAB and NOODLE STIR-FRY

Serves 4 Prep 10 mins Cook 12 mins

Ingredients

* 125g medium egg noodles
* 1 spray of low-cal cooking spray
* 300g pack of stir-fry vegetables (eg cabbage, peppers, onions, carrots and spring onions)
* 8 crabsticks, each sliced into three lengthways
* 2tbsp soy sauce

Method

1 Bring a pan of salted water to the boil, add the noodles and cook for 4 mins until softened. Drain.
2 Heat the low-cal cooking spray in a wok. Add the stir-fry vegetables and cook for 5 mins until just soft.
3 Stir in the noodles, crabsticks and soy sauce, and cook for a further 3-4 mins to warm through.

CALORIES 171

PESTO COD and VEGGIE PARCELS

Serves 4 Prep 10 mins Cook 20 mins

Ingredients

* 2 beef tomatoes, sliced
* Salt and ground black pepper
* 1 clove of garlic, crushed
* A small bunch of fresh basil
* 2 courgettes, cut into matchsticks
* 4 chunky cod steaks
* 8tsp fresh pesto sauce

Method

1 Preheat the oven to 200°C, Gas 6. Cut 4 large squares of greaseproof paper and place them in a roasting tin.
2 Put a few tomato slices into the centre of each square of paper, and season with salt and ground black pepper. Top with the garlic, basil and courgettes.
3 Arrange the cod steaks on top of the vegetables and spread with the pesto. Fold the paper over to make parcels.
4 Bake in the oven for 20 mins until the fish and vegetables are tender and cooked through. Serve in the parcels.

Smart tip

Serve with mashed potato on the side for non-dieters. Add 1 garlic clove to the water as the potatoes boil. Drain and mash with milk and a knob of low-fat spread. Season well.

CALORIES

200

SIMPLE RUSTIC SOUP

Serves 4 Prep 5 mins Cook 35 mins

Ingredients

* 1tbsp olive oil
* 1 onion, peeled and chopped
* 1 large carrot, peeled and diced
* 1 celery stick, chopped
* 1 clove of garlic, crushed
* 1 bay leaf
* 400g can of chopped tomatoes
* 410g can of borlotti or other beans, drained and rinsed
* 1ltr turkey or chicken stock
* 200g cooked ham, cut into bite-sized chunks
* Salt and ground black pepper
* Large handful of fresh parsley leaves, to garnish

Method

1 Heat the oil in a large pan. Add the onion, carrot and celery, and cook for 5 mins to soften. Add the garlic and bay leaf, and cook for a further 5 mins.
2 Stir in the chopped tomatoes, beans and stock. Simmer for 20 mins until the carrots are just tender.
3 Ladle half the soup into a blender and process until almost smooth. Return to the pan.
4 Add the chopped ham and cook for 5 mins until piping hot. Season to taste with salt and ground black pepper. Sprinkle with fresh parsley to serve.

Smart tip

Serve crusty French bread on the side for non-dieters. A 20g serving of bread is 50 cals so, if you weigh it out carefully and won't be tempted to have more, you could enjoy a mouthful too!

CALORIES

200

CHICKEN TIKKA MASALA

Serves 4 Prep 10 mins Cook 25 mins

Ingredients

* 1tbsp groundnut oil
* 1 red onion, sliced
* 350g chicken fillets
* 2tbsp tikka masala paste
  (depending on the strength
  of the brand)
* 200g can of chopped tomatoes
* Small bunch of fresh coriander
* 2 mini naan breads, to serve

Method

1 Heat the oil in a wok and gently fry the onion for 5 mins to soften. Add the chicken fillets and cook for 10 mins, turning, until browned.
2 Stir in the tikka masala paste and cook for 3 mins to 'cook off' the raw spice taste.
3 Add 100ml water and the chopped tomatoes. Warm through for 5 mins. Sprinkle with coriander sprigs and serve with a mini naan bread.

Smart tip

Other curry pastes that work well in this dish are korma, rogan josh and madras. This can be served with boiled basmati rice for non-dieters.

CALORIES

250

POTATO, EGG and CRESS SALAD

Serves 4 Prep 10 mins Cook 15 mins

Ingredients

* 450g new potatoes
* 4 eggs
* 3 celery sticks, chopped
* 150g radishes, thinly sliced
* 2tbsp fresh chives, snipped
* 1 punnet of mustard and cress
* 100ml Pizza Express Light Dressing

Method

1 Cook the potatoes in a pan of boiling salted water for 15 mins, until tender.
2 Meanwhile, plunge the eggs into boiling salted water, return to the boil and cook for 8 mins. Drain and cool the eggs quickly under cold running water, then shell and slice.
3 Put the potatoes and celery in a serving bowl. Top with the radishes, chives and mustard and cress. Drizzle with the dressing to serve.

Smart tip

Try quails' eggs instead of regular eggs. You can have 5 quails' eggs for 1 regular egg. They only take 2 mins to hard-boil.

CALORIES 247

CHILLI BEEF and BEAN SOUP

Serves 4 Prep 20 mins Cook 2 hrs 15 mins

Ingredients

* 1tbsp olive oil
* 1 onion, peeled and chopped
* 2 garlic cloves, peeled and crushed
* 250g stewing steak, cubed
* Salt and ground black pepper
* 2tsp mild chilli powder
* ½tsp ground cumin
* 400g can of chopped tomatoes
* 1.25ltr hot beef stock
* 200g butternut squash, peeled, deseeded and cut into 1cm cubes
* 1tbsp balsamic vinegar
* 400g can of cannellini beans, drained and rinsed
* 1tbsp chopped fresh parsley

Method

1 Preheat the oven to 180°C, Gas 4. Heat the oil in a large, flameproof casserole dish. Add the onion and cook for 3 mins to soften. Add the garlic and stewing steak, and fry for 5 mins to brown.

2 Season with salt and ground black pepper, and add the chilli powder and ground cumin. Stir well and continue to cook for 2 mins.

3 Add the chopped tomatoes, beef stock, butternut squash and balsamic vinegar. Bring to the boil, cover and transfer to the oven. Bake for 2 hrs, until the meat is really tender.

4 Stir in the cannellini beans and warm through on the hob. Serve sprinkled with chopped fresh parsley.

Smart tip

You can vary the meat according to what's available. Pork shoulder, leg of lamb or boneless, skinless chicken also work well – but be sure to adjust the cals (250g stewing steak is 562 cals).

CALORIES

250

HUNGER BUSTING VEGGIE BALTI

Serves 4 Prep 10 mins Cook 30 mins

Ingredients

* 1tbsp sunflower oil
* 2 onions, chopped
* 1tbsp balti paste
* 350g mixed diced butternut squash and sweet potato
* 400g can of chopped tomatoes
* ½ cauliflower, cut into florets
* Salt and ground black pepper
* 410g can of chickpeas, drained
* Handful of fresh coriander leaves

Method

1 Heat the sunflower oil in a large pan. Add the onions and fry gently for 5 mins, to soften. Add the balti paste and fry for a further 1 min.

2 Add the diced butternut squash and sweet potato, chopped tomatoes, cauliflower and 250ml water. Season with salt and ground black pepper. Cover and simmer for 15 mins, until the vegetables are tender.

3 Add the chickpeas and warm through for 5 mins. Sprinkle with coriander leaves to serve.

Smart tip

Serve non-dieters a toasted naan bread on the side – but don't be tempted to tuck into one yourself! Instead, make up your 250 cals with a piece of fruit for dessert.

CALORIES
211

AMERICAN DREAM PASTA SALAD

Serves 6 Prep 5 mins Cook 10 mins

Ingredients

* 200g fusilli
* 1tbsp American classic yellow mustard
* 4tbsp light Italian dressing
* 6 gherkins, sliced
* 18 cherry tomatoes, halved
* 8 slices pastrami
* 3tbsp chopped fresh parsley

Method

1 Cook the pasta in a large pan of boiling salted water for 10 mins, until tender.
2 Meanwhile, put the mustard in a large bowl, and whisk in the Italian dressing. Add the gherkins, cherry tomatoes, pastrami and parsley.
3 Drain the pasta and stir into the salad. Serve warm or cold.

CALORIES

210

EASY BEEF STEW

Serves 4 Prep 5 mins Cook 1 hr 30 mins

Ingredients

* 450g stewing beef
* 1 red onion, cut into wedges
* 2 garlic cloves, sliced
* 2 sprigs of fresh parsley or thyme, plus extra leaves to garnish
* 300g baby carrots
* 450ml hot beef stock
* 2tbsp sundried tomato paste
* 2tbsp balsamic vinegar
* 2tbsp gravy granules

Method

1 Preheat the oven to 180°C, Gas 4. Place all the ingredients in a large casserole dish and stir to combine.
2 Cook in the oven for 1 hr 30 mins, until the meat and vegetables are tender. Sprinkle with the rest of the fresh herbs to serve.

Smart tip

This recipe works well in a slow cooker. Put everything in the pot and set on low for 6-8 hrs. Perfect when you're out at work all day – come home to a hot, healthy meal.

CALORIES

240

SIMPLE SPANISH OMELETTE

Serves 4 Prep 10 mins Cook 15 mins

Ingredients

* 1tbsp olive oil
* 300g can of Jersey potatoes, rinsed and drained
* 200g red onions, sliced
* 5 eggs, lightly beaten
* 8 slices of chorizo
* Salt and ground black pepper
* 2tbsp chopped fresh parsley

Method

1 Heat the oil in a heavy-based frying pan. Add the potatoes and onions and fry for 5 mins to soften.

2 Pour in the eggs and scatter with the chorizo slices. Season with salt and ground black pepper. Cook for 5 mins until the base is firm.

3 Put the pan under a hot grill for 5 mins, until the eggs are firm. Sprinkle with the chopped parsley to serve.

Smart tip

This recipe uses canned potatoes to save you time. However, if you prefer to use fresh, boil 200g new or salad potatoes for 15 mins until tender. Drain well.

CALORIES

241

CHICKEN and CASHEW STIR-FRY

Serves 4 Prep 10 mins Cook 10 mins

Ingredients

* 50g cashew nuts
* 1tbsp vegetable oil
* 1 red onion, sliced
* 1 yellow pepper, deseeded and chopped
* 400g skinless chicken breast fillets, cut into bite-sized pieces
* 1 garlic clove, crushed
* 1cm fresh ginger, grated
* 175g Tenderstem broccoli, cut into 2cm pieces
* 3tbsp soy sauce
* 1tbsp sweet chilli sauce

Method

1 Heat a wok or large frying pan until hot. Add the cashew nuts and stir-fry for 30 secs until golden, then remove from the pan.
2 Heat the oil in the pan. Add the onion and pepper, and fry for 1 min. Add the chicken and stir-fry for 3 mins until browned and almost cooked through.
3 Add the garlic, ginger and broccoli, and stir-fry for 1 min. Add 2tbsp water, cover and cook for 2 mins.
4 Add the soy sauce and sweet chilli sauce, stir and heat through for 1 min. Scatter with the toasted cashews.

Smart tip

Why not swap the chicken for chunks of chicken-style Quorn? There are 424 cals in 400g skinless chicken breast, but only 356 cals in the Quorn equivalent.

CALORIES
250

SAUSAGES with ROASTED RATATOUILLE

Serves 6 Prep 15 mins Cook 40 mins

Ingredients

* 12 reduced-fat sausages
* 2 small red onions, cut into wedges
* 2 garlic cloves, crushed
* 200g courgettes, chopped
* 1 aubergine, chopped
* 1 yellow pepper, deseeded and chopped
* A few sprigs of fresh rosemary
* 1tbsp olive oil
* 200g cherry tomatoes

Method

1 Preheat the oven to 200°C, Gas 6. Put the sausages in a large roasting tin (or 2 smaller ones) and cook in the oven for 5 mins.

2 Add the onion wedges, garlic, courgettes, aubergine and peppers to the tin. Scatter with the rosemary sprigs and drizzle with the olive oil. Roast in the oven for 25 mins.

3 Turn the sausages and vegetables. Add the tomatoes and return to the oven for a further 5 mins, until the veg is tender and the sausages are golden. Serve immediately.

Smart tip

Serve with cous cous for non-dieters. Put 200ml hot vegetable stock in a bowl. Add 100g cous cous, cover and leave to stand until the liquid is absorbed. Fluff up with a fork. (Serves 1.)

CALORIES

250

LEMONY CHICKEN with VEG COUS COUS

Serves 4 Prep 15 mins Cook 10 mins

Ingredients

* 4 boneless, skinless chicken breasts
* Salt and ground black pepper
* 2 lemons
* 2 garlic cloves, crushed
* 100g roasted vegetable cous cous
* A handful of chopped fresh mint, plus extra mint leaves to garnish

Method

1 Season the chicken generously with salt and ground black pepper. Juice and finely zest 1 lemon. Coat the chicken in the lemon zest and juice and the crushed garlic.

2 Heat a non-stick pan and pan-fry the chicken for 10 mins, turning as needed, until golden all over.

3 Meanwhile, make up the cous cous with hot water, according to packet instructions. Squeeze in the juice of ½ lemon and add a generous handful of chopped mint.

4 Cut the remaining ½ lemon into wedges. Slice the chicken and serve with the cous cous, garnished with extra mint leaves.

Smart tip

Buy a non-stick Teflon sheet and use for low-cal roasting. Place the lemony chicken on the sheet and roast in the oven for 10 mins at 210°C, Gas 7. It saves on washing up too!

CALORIES

242

SPINACH and CHEESE SOUFFLE OMELETTE

Serves 1 Prep 10 mins Cook 8 mins

Ingredients

* 100g baby spinach leaves, rinsed
* 2 medium eggs, separated
* Salt and ground black pepper
* 1 spray of Frylight one-cal cooking spray
* 15g low-fat Cheddar, grated
* 1tsp sweet chilli jam, to serve

Method

1 Put the spinach in a bowl and microwave on High for 2 mins, to wilt. Transfer to a sieve and press to squeeze out any excess liquid.

2 Whisk the egg whites until the mixture forms soft peaks.

3 Preheat the grill to high. Beat the egg yolks with 3tbsp cold water, and season with salt and ground black pepper. Gently fold the egg whites into the yolk mixture.

4 Heat a small non-stick frying pan and spray with Frylight. Tip in the soufflé omelette mixture and cook for 3 mins until the base is firm.

5 Sprinkle with the grated cheese and wilted spinach leaves. Put the pan under a hot grill for 3 mins until the top of the omelette is firm. Serve immediately with the sweet chilli jam.

Smart tip

Swap the spinach for rocket or watercress to save time. Add raw to the soufflé omelette just before serving.

CALORIES

250

STEAK with BALSAMIC TOMATOES

Serves 2 Prep 5 mins Cook 10 mins

Ingredients

* 3 sprays of Frylight one-cal cooking spray
* 1 garlic clove, crushed
* 200g cherry tomatoes
* Pinch of caster sugar
* 1tbsp chopped fresh basil leaves
* Salt and ground black pepper
* 2 rump steaks (150g each), trim off fat
* 100g wild rocket leaves
* 1tbsp Parmesan shavings
* 2tsp balsamic vinegar

Method

1 Heat 1 spray of Frylight in a non-stick frying pan. Add the garlic, tomatoes, sugar and chopped basil. Season with salt and ground black pepper and fry for 5 mins until tomatoes are softened.
2 Meanwhile, heat a griddle pan. Spray the steaks on both sides with Frylight and season well with salt and ground black pepper. Fry for 2-4 mins on each side for medium rare. If you prefer it well done, cook for a few extra mins on each side. Transfer to warm plates and rest for 5 mins.
3 Serve the steaks and roasted tomatoes with the rocket leaves and Parmesan shavings. Drizzle with balsamic vinegar and any steak juices.

CALORIES
250

VEGETABLE BOLOGNESE

Serves 4 Prep 15 mins Cook 25 mins

Ingredients

* 1tbsp olive oil
* 1 red onion, chopped
* 1 large garlic clove, crushed
* 3 carrots, chopped
* 1 red pepper, deseeded and chopped
* 75g mushrooms, sliced
* 500g carton of creamed tomatoes
* 75g broccoli, broken into florets
* 1tbsp Worcestershire sauce
* A pinch of sugar
* 2tbsp fresh basil leaves
* Salt and ground black pepper
* 150g dried spaghetti

Method

1 Heat the oil in a large pan. Add the onion and cook for 5 mins to soften. Add the garlic and carrots, and cook for 5 mins. Add the peppers and cook for a further 2 mins.

2 Stir in the mushrooms, creamed tomatoes, broccoli, Worcestershire sauce and sugar. Add most of the basil leaves and 200ml water. Season with salt and ground black pepper and simmer for 5 mins.

3 Meanwhile, cook the spaghetti in boiling salted water for 10 mins until tender, but still with a slight bite.

4 Tip half the vegetable mixture into a food processor and blend until almost smooth. Return to the pan and stir together while warming through. Drain the spaghetti and toss into the vegetable sauce. Garnish with a few extra basil leaves to serve.

CALORIES
232

BEAN SALAD with MUSTARD DRESSING

Serves 6 Prep 10 mins Cook 2 mins

Ingredients

* ✱ 90g green beans, trimmed and halved
* ✱ 1 red onion, peeled and chopped
* ✱ 2 sticks of celery, chopped
* ✱ 410g can of cannellini beans, rinsed and drained
* ✱ 410g can of borlotti beans, rinsed and drained
* ✱ 6 cherry tomatoes, halved

For the dressing

* ✱ 2tbsp wholegrain mustard
* ✱ 1tbsp clear honey
* ✱ Finely grated zest and juice of 1 lemon
* ✱ 4tbsp olive oil
* ✱ Salt and ground black pepper

Method

1 Put the green beans in a heatproof bowl with 2tbsp water. Cover with cling film, pierce and microwave on High for 2 mins. Rinse in cold water and place in a large bowl.

2 Rinse the chopped red onion in a sieve to remove the strong flavour, then add to the bowl. Mix in the celery, canned beans and tomatoes.

3 To make the dressing, put the mustard, honey, lemon zest and juice and oil in a small jar. Season with salt and ground black pepper and shake to mix. Drizzle over the salad.

CALORIES 180

SMOKED HADDOCK
and LEEK PIE

Serves 6 Prep 10 mins Cook 30 mins

Ingredients

* 1 leek, sliced
* 400g frozen skinless smoked haddock fillet
* 500g frozen skinless cod fillet
* 450ml semi-skimmed milk
* Salt and ground black pepper
* 3tbsp thickening granules
* 4 splashes of Tabasco sauce
* Small bunch of fresh basil
* 50g lemon and pepper breadcrumbs
* 1 lemon, sliced
* 1tbsp olive oil

Method

1 Preheat the oven to 200°C, Gas 6. Put the sliced leek in a bowl with 2tbsp water. Cover with cling film, pierce and microwave on High for 5 mins to soften. Drain.

2 Put the haddock and cod in a frying pan and pour over the milk. Season generously with salt and ground black pepper. Cover and simmer for 5 mins.

3 Lift the fish out of the milk and put in the base of an ovenproof dish with the drained leeks.

4 Add the thickening granules and Tabasco sauce to the milk. Heat and stir until thickened.

5 Sprinkle a few basil leaves over the fish, pour over the thickened sauce, and scatter with the breadcrumbs. Arrange the lemon slices on top and drizzle with the olive oil.

6 Bake for 20 mins until golden. Top with a few more basil leaves, to serve.

CALORIES
232

TUNA PASTA SALAD WITH EGG

Serves 2 Prep 10 mins Cook 10 mins

Ingredients

* 100g penne pasta
* 1 egg
* 100g French beans
* ¼ cucumber, chopped
* 6 cherry tomatoes, halved
* 70g tuna in brine, drained
* 1tbsp Pizza Express light dressing
* 1tbsp white wine vinegar

Method

1 Cook the pasta in boiling salted water for 7 mins.
2 In a separate pan put the egg into boiling salted water, return to the boil and cook for 8 mins.
3 Add the beans to the pasta for the last 3 mins or until just tender.
4 Drain the pasta and beans and cool quickly under cold running water. Run the hard-boiled egg under cold running water too, then cut in half.
5 Put the pasta, beans, tomatoes, tuna and dressing in a large bowl, season and stir to mix. Top with eggs to serve.

Smart tip

If you prefer to serve this meal for lunch instead of dinner halve the quantity of pasta to 50g. Bulk it up with some more cucumber if you want to give it extra crunch!

CALORIES
250

SPEEDY TERIYAKI STIR-FRY WTH STEAK

Serves 2 Prep 10 mins Cook 10 mins

Ingredients

* 150g fillet steak
* 2tbsp teriyaki sauce
* 1tsp sesame oil
* 1tsp 'very lazy' garlic
* 300g stir-fry vegetables
* ¼ cucumber, cut into matchsticks
* 2tbsp fresh coriander leaves

Method

1 Season steak well with salt and ground black pepper, then pour over 1tbsp teriyaki sauce.

2 Meanwhile, heat a heavy-based pan or griddle and fry steak for 5 mins, turning it to seal and brown all the edges. Remove from pan, place on a plate and leave to rest for 5 mins.

3 Heat sesame oil in a large non-stick wok. Add garlic and stir-fry for 5 mins.

4 Divide vegetables between two plates, sprinkle over cucumber and remaining 1tbsp teriyaki sauce. Slice steak and serve on top of vegetables, sprinkled with fresh coriander.

Smart tip

For a cheaper alternative to steak use pork loin fillet. Bash between greaseproof paper to make a thin escalope and cook for 10 mins until no longer pink. A thicker fillet will take at least 15-20 mins to cook.

CALORIES

VEGETABLE MIXED GRILL

Serves 2 Prep 10 mins Cook 15 mins

Ingredients

* 125g Portobellini mushrooms or other mushrooms of your choice
* 1 large beef tomato, sliced
* 1 red pepper, de-seeded and cut into wedges
* 125g reduced fat mozzarella, drained and sliced
* 1 garlic clove, sliced
* Fresh basil leaves
* 1tbsp olive oil

Method

1 Preheat the grill to high.
2 Spread the Portobellini mushrooms (or mushrooms of your choice), the sliced tomatoes and wedges of pepper with space apart over a grill pan or baking tray. Top each tomato with some of the mozzarella, sprinkle over the garlic and top with a basil leaf.
3 Season it all generously with salt and ground black pepper, drizzle over a little olive oil and place under the hot grill for 10-15 mins or until all the vegetables are tender and the mozzarella cheese has just melted.

Smart tip

Try grilling the mushrooms with garlic and half the olive oil and serve the tomato, peppers, mozzarella and basil on the side as a salad, drizzled with a little balsamic vinegar.

CALORIES 250

MOROCCAN ROOT TAGINE with COUS COUS

Dinner

Serves 2 Prep 10 mins Cook 1 Hr 5 mins

Ingredients

* 1tsp cumin seeds, crushed
* 1tsp coriander seeds, crushed
* 400g can chopped tomatoes
* 2 leeks, sliced
* 2 courgettes, sliced
* 2 carrots, peeled, chopped
* ½ x 400g can chickpeas, drained
* 1 level tsp turmeric
* Salt and ground black pepper
* 50g wholewheat cous cous
* Coriander, to garnish

Method

1 Set the oven to 180°C, 350°F, Gas 4. Heat a solid-based pan and add the cumin and coriander seeds. Cook for about 20-30 secs, stirring all the time, until you can begin to smell the seeds.

2 Pour in the canned tomatoes and 300ml water and bring to the boil. Add the leeks, courgettes, carrots and chickpeas to the pan. Stir in the turmeric and seasoning to combine.

3 Transfer the vegetable mixture to a tagine (or divide between 2 individual tagines), or a casserole dish with a lid, and cook in the oven for about 1 hour, or until all the vegetables are soft.

4 Tip the cous cous into a bowl and pour over 75ml boiling water and stir well. Leave the cous cous for about 5 mins, until it's softened, gently stirring it occasionally. Garnish the tagine with coriander and serve with the cous cous.

Smart tip

The cous cous amounts for 90 calories per portion in this recipe, so if you serve this without it you can have a great low calorie lunch too.

CALORIES

238

FLASH-IN-THE-PAN LEMON LAMB

Serves 4 Prep 10 mins Cook 15 mins

Ingredients

* 4 x 100g lamb cutlets, fat trimmed off
* Finely grated zest and juice of 1 lemon
* 2 garlic cloves, crushed
* 1tsp dried oregano
* 1 leek, washed and sliced
* 150ml vegetable stock
* 100g green beans, trimmed
* 400g can cannellini beans, rinsed and drained
* Lemon wedges, to serve

Method

1 Preheat the grill to medium high. Place the lamb cutlets on a grill pan lined with a non-stick Teflon sheet.

2 Season the lamb generously with salt and ground black pepper. Sprinkle over the lemon zest and juice, garlic and oregano and grill for 10 mins, turning the cutlets halfway through.

3 Meanwhile, dry-fry the sliced leeks in a non-stick pan on a low heat for 10 mins or until they are softened.

4 Pour the vegetable stock into the pan with the leeks and then add the green beans and cannellini beans. Cook gently for a few mins until warmed through.

5 Season the beans and serve with the cooked cutlets and extra wedges of lemon, if you like.

Smart tip

Look out for lamb neck fillet or lamb leg steaks instead of cutlets. These save time as they don't have any visible fat to be trimmed off. Serve a maximum size of 100g per person.

CALORIES

250

CITRUS BAKED FISH WITH COURGETTES

Serves 2 Prep 10 mins Cook 25 mins

Ingredients

* 1 courgette, cut into matchsticks
* 1/3 garlic clove, crushed
* 1tbsp chopped basil
* 1tbsp olive oil
* 4 cherry tomatoes
* 2 white fish fillets
* 1/2 lemon, zested, then cut into wedges
* Pinch of crushed dried chilli
* 2tbsp breadcrumbs
* 1tbsp flat-leaf parsley, chopped

Method

1 Heat oven to 200°C, 400°F, Gas 6. Put courgettes into an ovenproof dish. Sprinkle over half the garlic, the basil, 1tsp oil and the tomatoes. Place fish and lemon wedges on top and season.
2 Heat the rest of the oil in a pan, then add remaining garlic and the chilli. Cook for 2 mins. Add zest, breadcrumbs and parsley and fry until crisp.
3 Sprinkle over fish and roast for 20 mins until cooked through.

Smart tip

For men (or non-fast days), serve with 100g of boiled new potatoes which will add an extra 75 calories.

CALORIES

222

10 FAST DINNERS

Tempt your tastebuds with these quick and easy supper dishes...

1 QUORN MEATBALLS

Cook 4 Quorn meat-free Swedish Style Balls from chilled in the microwave with 100g tomato pasta sauce. Serve with a green salad made from mixed leaves, such as watercress, oak leaf lettuce, rocket and sliced cucumber. Squeeze over some lemon juice and season with ground black pepper.

170 calories

2 GRILLED LIME AND GARLIC CHICKEN IN A WRAP

Season 75g chicken breast, and sprinkle with the finely grated zest and juice of ½ lime and 1 crushed garlic clove. Cook under a preheated grill for 15 mins, turning chicken halfway through. Slice and serve in 1 medium sized wrap (60g) with 25g shredded iceberg lettuce.

240 calories

3 SCRAMBLED EGGS ON TOAST

Lightly beat 2 eggs with 2tbsp skimmed milk, and season to taste with salt and ground black pepper. Heat, stirring, for 2-3 mins until almost firm. Toast 1 slice (22g) of diet bread and serve topped with the scrambled eggs.

235 calories

4 MUSHROOMS ON TOAST

Fry 150g sliced button mushrooms in 1tsp olive oil for 5 mins. Serve on 2 slices of wholemeal toast.

207 calories

9 GOAT'S CHEESE OMELETTE
Beat 2 eggs with 2tbsp cold water. Heat 1tsp oil in a frying pan and add the eggs. Cook for 3 mins until the base is firm. Add 15g chopped goat's cheese. Cook for a further 1 min, until melted.

250 calories

5 COD WITH PESTO AND BEANS
Spread a 175g cod fillet with 1tsp pesto and grill for 10 mins. Serve with 100g boiled green beans.

190 calories

7 BAKED BEANS ON TOAST
Warm 200g Weight Watchers baked beans. Serve on 1 slice of wholemeal toast.

226 calories

10 SMOKED HADDOCK WITH POTATOES AND BROCCOLI
Boil 100g potatoes and 75g broccoli. Grill 100g smoked haddock for 10 mins until cooked through. Add a squeeze of lemon juice to serve.

178 calories

6 FISH FINGERS
Grill 3 fish fingers. Serve with 50g boiled new potatoes and 50g frozen peas, boiled. Season to taste.

200 calories

8 GAMMON AND SWEETCORN
Grill a 100g gammon steak, trimmed of all fat, for 15 mins. Serve with 50g tinned sweetcorn.

250 calories

SNACK ATTACK

Help yourself to these low-cal treats...

44 calories

Miso soup (1 sachet)

31 calories

Cup of air-popped corn

50 calories

10 green olives (30g)

55 calories

10g dark chocolate

50 calories

1 small scoop of
vanilla ice cream

90 calories

1 Ski mango mousse
(59g pot)

70 calories

1 oatcake spread with
1tsp peanut butter

90 calories

2 ginger biscuits

70 calories

Funsize Milky Way

77 calories

Thin slice of malt loaf (25g)

50 calories

5 salt&vinegar Pringles

31 calories

1 Cadbury choc finger

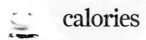

85 calories

125ml red or white wine

77 calories

1 Weight Watchers choc & toffee mini pot swirl

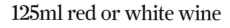

40 calories

Cup of low-cal hot chocolate, ie Options

46 calories

2 slices of ham (50g)

45 calories

1 jaffa cake

46 calories

2 marshmallows

49 calories

16 cherry tomatoes

41 calories

Small pack of raisins (15g)

42 calories

1 Mini Babybel Light

45 calories

1 slice pineapple (100g)

35 calories

5 almonds

50 calories

10 asparagus spears (200g)

49 calories

1/4 tin of Heinz baked beans

6 calories

Hartley's No Added Sugar Strawberry Jelly (115g pot)

45 calories

7 carrot sticks with 1tbsp low-fat ranch dressing

58 calories

2 kiwis

47 calories

1 Refreshers ice lolly

95 calories

1 small banana (100g)

48 calories

20 blackberries

88 calories

Bag of Quavers (16.4g)

25 calories

1 Laughing Cow
light triangle

80 calories

20 cherries (175g)

90 calories

4 slices of fresh mango

75 calories

1 Starbucks tall skimmed
milk cappuccino

98 calories

Small bag of
Twiglets (24g)

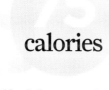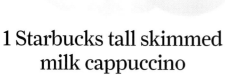

100 calories

One medium size corn
on the cob

IT WORKED *for us!*

Just how easy is it to fit living on 500 calories on two days a week into your lifestyle? We asked real women to reveal their top tips...

'LEMON SLICES ARE A LIFESAVER'

Andrea McEvoy, 37, a nurse from Middlesbrough, is married with a teenage son. She started the 5:2 diet in June, and lost almost 2st to reach her 9st target by October.

Keep slices of oranges and lemons in the fridge: They help to take the plainness out of water when you're drinking so much of it to fill up.
Stock up on jelly: These low-cal snacks are great for beating off hunger and satisfying sweet cravings. Sugar-free jelly cubes are just 10 cals each.
Plan ahead: Think about the next couple of days, and consider when post-work tiredness may mean you don't feel like cooking. I love my slow cooker for post-work nights as it's so easy to whip up something delicious and nutritious, and have it ready and waiting for me when I get in.
The freezer is your friend: When making meals, put a portion in a foil dish and freeze it for fast days. I love homemade soups and chillis, which are easy to defrost and can be prepared in minutes.

Keep exercise light on fast days:
I still exercise when I'm fasting, but only gentle classes such as Pilates. I save the energetic classes for non-fast days. Not only does exercise help keep you trim, it also keeps your mind off your fast.

FACTS
WEIGHT BEFORE:
10st 12lb
WEIGHT AFTER:
9st
TOTAL LOSS:
1st 12lb

BEFORE

'BOVRIL IS BRILL'

Jo Alderman, 43, is a married mum of one from Fleetwood, Lancashire. She's lost 2st.

Get into hot Bovril: On fast days, it fills me up and means I can save my calories for an evening meal.
Beat hunger with sparkling water: I didn't suffer much with hunger, but when I feel the odd pang, I drink a large glass of sparkling water and it quickly passes.
Fill up on chilli: I love skinny chilli con carne. It's really filling, even without any rice.
Start as you mean to go on: As soon as I read *The 5:2 Diet Book* by Kate Harrison, I started fasting the next day. I haven't looked back, going from 11st 5lb to 9st 5lb.

BEFORE

FACTS
WEIGHT BEFORE:
12st 4lb
WEIGHT AFTER:
9st 4lb
TOTAL LOSS:
3st

WITH THANKS TO KATE HARRISON'S 5:2 DIET FACEBOOK PAGE. *THE 5:2 DIET BOOK* BY KATE HARRISON (£6.99, ORION)

FACTS

WEIGHT BEFORE:
11st 5lb

WEIGHT AFTER:
9st 5lb

TOTAL LOSS:
2st

'CARBS PUSH THE HUNGER BUTTON'

Christine Curry, 52, is a personal assistant from Bury St Edmunds, Suffolk, and is married with two grown-up sons and two step-daughters. She started the 5:2 diet to slim down for a holiday, and has now lost 2st.

Drink lots of fluids when you're fasting: Water, green or black tea and black coffee will all help to fill you up.
Avoid carbs on fast days: I always found that rather than filling me up, carbohydrates just switched on my 'hunger button'.
Chicken keeps me satisfied: I love Mediterranean roasted vegetables with chicken or fish, or Spanish-style chicken bake without the potatoes.
There's always tomorrow: When you're feeling really hungry, focus on the fact that tomorrow, you can have a full English if you want. That's the beauty of the diet – you can eat whatever you want on the other five days of the week.
Accept that there's no life after 5:2: The diet is a lifestyle change, and accepting that makes it easier to deal with this new way of eating. I've now reached my target weight, and gone from 11st 12lb to 9st 12lb. I maintain my shape with a 6:1 week, but I do go back to fasting whenever I need to.

FACTS

WEIGHT BEFORE:
11st 12lb

WEIGHT AFTER:
9st 12lb

TOTAL LOSS:
3st

'THE 5:2 MAKES ME FEEL YOUNGER'

Linda Christie, 63, is a divorced mum of three from Ashford, Kent. She started the diet in 2012 and dropped from size 16 to size 10. Linda now maintains her weight with one fast day a week.

Go as long as you can without eating on a fast day: I just have an evening meal – as soon as I eat anything, I've 'awoken the beast' and start thinking about food.
Soup is super: I love soups, especially curried sweet potato and lentil, and curried parsnip. But I don't like zero noodles – I'd rather just go without.
Beat hunger by staying out of the house: A long walk, run or trip to the cinema keeps hunger at bay, as you're not tempted to nip to the fridge.
Start exercising: This diet has given me much more energy. I've even started running three times a week because I felt so brilliant, and I walk miles every day. I feel so much younger than 63.
It's a way of life not a diet: In the past I'd have stopped 'dieting' and put all the weight back on. I lost 3st and I still fast one day a week to maintain my figure. Think of it as a lifestyle choice, not a means to an end.

Neurocare Products

Lynda Bellingham, OBE Wants To Give You 21 Reasons To Use Neurocare 21

We know that Glucosamine helps to protect our bones why would we not want the same protection for our brains? This was the reason why Barbara Hobbs, after her brave struggle to overcome her own Stroke, researched and created a natural product to help protect and nourish the brain from Stroke and early Dementia, using

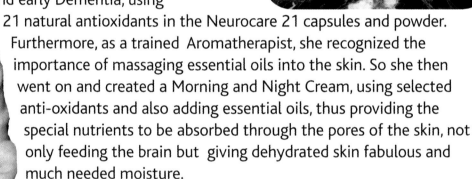

21 natural antioxidants in the Neurocare 21 capsules and powder. Furthermore, as a trained Aromatherapist, she recognized the importance of massaging essential oils into the skin. So she then went on and created a Morning and Night Cream, using selected anti-oxidants and also adding essential oils, thus providing the special nutrients to be absorbed through the pores of the skin, not only feeding the brain but giving dehydrated skin fabulous and much needed moisture.

"Having used the Neurocare Products for the last three years, and introduced them to my family and friends I can happily say we will be using them for years to come."

For more information and ordering:
www.neurocareproducts.com • E-mail:**info@neurocareproducts.com** • Tel: **0845 557 7160**

I first met Barbara in 2007 when she received the Adult Courage Award from the Stroke Association. Her story was quite remarkable. She had got up as usual one morning and made herself a cup of tea but as she drank it she realised she was dribbling. Thanks to her nursing training she knew immediately she was having a stroke. She lost the use of her right side as she struggled to reach the phone but using her left hand dialled 999 only to then collapse, and suffer a further stroke that immobilised her left side.

For the next six months Barbara refused to give up. She taught herself how the brain worked and what it needed to protect and nourish itself. She found twenty one anti-oxidants that were beneficial to the brain. However, as Barbara herself points out "To get enough nourishment from all the vegetables involved, you would need to consume an entire field's worth every day!"

So, she found herself a biochemist that could produce a powder compound which is now available as a capsule.

Next time I met Barbara was in my dressing room at the Grand theatre in Leeds on my nationwide tour of Calendar Girls. I was so inspired by her story, and all her hard work, I wanted to help in some way. So my husband Michael suggested we help her with her start-up costs and that I would use my name to endorse the products and raise her profile. What a team we made! It has taken three years getting the range up and running and passed by the Trading Standards Authority but now Neurocare products are available on the internet. Not just the capsule but the wonderful moisturising creams as well.

Barbara is the best advert there could possibly be, not just for her example of triumph over adversity, but proof that the capsule really does work.

What to eat on NORMAL DAYS...

Maximise your weight loss with our guide to what to eat on your non-fast days...

One thing that makes the 5:2 diet so easy to follow is the fact it doesn't feel like you're on a diet. On fast days you can comfort yourself knowing that for five days you can eat what you like, within reason. We recommend that you aim to eat around 2,000 calories on non-fast days and continue to stick to a largely healthy, balanced diet. But because your intake of vitamins and minerals will be less on fast days, you'll need to top up on your normal days.

Our five days of menus (on the next page) show you the foods you can eat on non-fast days. You'll see they are fairly healthy – with a few treats included – and below is our guide to what a 'healthy diet' should include.

KEEP PROTEINS LOW IN FAT
Low-fat sources of protein include lean meat, poultry, fish, eggs, beans, pulses, lentils and vegetarian meat substitutes. Nuts and seeds are also a good source of healthy protein.

CHOOSE WHOLEGRAINS
Your body's preferred source of energy is starchy carbohydrates. You can get it from wholegrains, such as wholemeal bread, brown rice, wholemeal pasta, oats and other wholegrain cereals. These are more nutritious than their 'white' counterparts, plus they're higher in fibre. This means they have a lower glycaemic index (GI), so they break down and release their energy more slowly to help maintain stable blood sugar levels. They'll also keep you feeling fuller for longer.

FILL UP YOUR PLATE WITH VEG
Most vegetables are low in calories and virtually fat-free, plus they're packed with vitamins, minerals and antioxidants, which are essential for good health.

EAT ENOUGH HEALTHY FATS
Fat will be cut down to the bare minimum on fast days. On the other days make sure that you're getting enough healthy, unsaturated fats from olive oil, avocados, nuts and seeds (and their oils), and oily fish such as salmon, mackerel and fresh tuna. Some fats are essential for health – as long as they're from the right sources.

MAXIMISE THE FRUIT
Fruit is another good source of vitamins, minerals and healthy plant compounds. It's also a great way to indulge a sweet craving.

GET ENOUGH FLUIDS
Make sure you keep hydrated. Water is the most hydrating, but tea and coffee count too. Fruit juice is quite high in fruit sugars (so always dilute it and only drink with meals), but it's also packed with vitamins. Milk is a useful source of the calcium we need to maintain healthy bones.

DAY 1

2,017 calories

BREAKFAST

✱ Two-egg mushroom omelette. Slice of wholemeal toast with low-fat olive spread or marmalade. Cup of tea or coffee with milk. **525 cals**

MORNING SNACK

✱ Small packet of unsalted nuts and raisins. **115 cals**

LUNCH

✱ Box of sushi (334 cals). Bunch of grapes (58 cals). Packet of Sunbites (120 cals). **Total: 512 cals**

WALKERS
SUNBITES
SWEET CHILLI

AFTERNOON SNACK

✱ Round of Mini Babybel. **62 cals**

DINNER

✱ Medium steak, grilled (240 cals) with oven chips (190 cals) and a large salad (40 cals). Small (125ml) glass of wine (85 cals). 2 oatcakes or crackers (100 cals), some celery sticks with half a 125g pack of low-fat Boursin cheese (108 cals) and some grapes (40 cals). **Total: 803 cals**

Steak, chips and a glass of vino!

DAY 2

1,982 calories

BREAKFAST

✱ 2 Weetabix with semi-skimmed milk. Kiwi fruit. Cup of tea or coffee with milk. **265 cals**

MORNING SNACK

✱ 2 jaffa cakes. **90 cals**

LUNCH

✱ Pasta salad with tuna and sweetcorn – homemade or healthy options range (340 cals). Two-finger KitKat (107 cals) and an apple (55 cals). **Total: 502 cals**

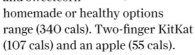

AFTERNOON SNACK

✱ None – save yourself for dinner tonight! Or save the apple or KitKat from lunchtime.

DINNER

✱ Pasta puttanesca (450 cals) with a slice of garlic bread (150 cals) and a salad (56 cals). Profiteroles (350 cals). Medium (175ml) glass of wine (119 cals). **Total: 1,125 cals**

Go out for an Italian!

DAY 3

2,020 calories

BREAKFAST

✱ Bowl of muesli with semi-skimmed milk, topped with a grated apple. Cup of tea or coffee with milk. **279 cals**

MORNING SNACK

✱ Medium skinny latte (114 cals). Square of chocolate brownie (335 cals). **Total: 449 cals**

LUNCH

✱ Wholemeal pitta stuffed with prawns and watercress, dressed with low-fat salad cream (318 cals). Slice of malt loaf (70 cals). Packet of Hula Hoops (129 cals). **Total: 517 cals**

AFTERNOON SNACK

✱ 37g bag Maltesers or a Crunchie. **150 cals**

Maltesers
Chocolate? Oh, go on then!

DINNER

✱ Quorn (or other vegetarian) chilli con carne (homemade with Quorn or tinned lentils, or from a healthy options range) with brown rice (450 cals). Griddled pineapple rings with a scoop of vanilla ice cream (175 cals). **Total: 625 cals**

DAY 4
1,826 calories

BREAKFAST
✱ Bowl of bran flakes with semi-skimmed milk, topped with a sliced banana. Cup of tea or coffee with milk. **309 cals**

MORNING SNACK
✱ 2 rice cakes spread with chocolate hazelnut spread. **130 cals**

LUNCH
✱ 6 chicken nuggets or a hamburger (250 cals), medium fries (330 cals), and a medium Diet Coke (4 cals).
Total: 584 cals

Midweek takeaway treat!

AFTERNOON SNACK
✱ 250ml fruit smoothie (homemade or shop-bought). **133 cals**

DINNER
✱ Chicken chop suey (homemade or from a healthy options range) with egg or soba noodles (450 cals). Half a tin of rice pudding with some sliced mango (220 cals). **Total: 670 cals**

DAY 5
2,100 calories

BREAKFAST
✱ Tin of sardines in tomato sauce, mashed with a dash of Worcestershire sauce, on 2 slices of wholemeal toast. Small glass of pure orange juice. Cup of tea or coffee with milk. **509 cals**

MORNING SNACK
✱ Small pot of fat-free natural yogurt (81 cals) topped with 1tsp honey (17 cals). **Total: 98 cals**

Shopping with a friend

LUNCH
✱ Mozzarella and sun-dried tomato panini with salad and coleslaw (450 cals). Small square (or half a slice) of iced carrot cake (220 cals). Small cappuccino (90 cals).
Total: 760 cals

AFTERNOON SNACK
✱ Large pot of air-popped popcorn with a pinch of cayenne pepper or paprika. **100 cals**

DINNER
✱ Grilled salmon steak (225 cals) with potato wedges (233 cals) and steamed broccoli (25 cals). Eton mess made with fat-free Greek yogurt, a crushed meringue shell and tinned or frozen berries (150 cals). **Total: 633 cals**

DIET TIPS FOR NORMAL DAYS

✱ On days when you're splurging on a meal out, lunch with a friend or a fancy coffee with a naughty cake, try to eat extra healthily for the rest of the day.

✱ Don't get hung up on trying to make each day's total add up to exactly 2,000 calories – it's the overall average that matters.

✱ At 85 cals, a small (125ml) glass of wine would take up a large chunk of a fast day's calories. But you can treat yourself a few days of the week if you factor them into your calorie allowance. Just don't exceed the safe limit of 14 units a week.

✱ Give yourself a pat on the back when you have a healthy snack like fruit, nuts or oatcakes with honey, instead of crisps or chocolate. You get more for your calories – a huge bunch of grapes has the same calories as a few squares of chocolate.

✱ If a chocolate craving does strike, these are the days when you can give in – within reason!

Calorie Counter

Food	Average portion (g)	Calories
FRUIT		
Apples	125	59
Apricots (flesh only)	80	25
Bananas	100	95
Blackberries	100	25
Blueberries	50	35
Cherries (weighed with stones)	80	38
Clementines (weighed with peel and pips)	80	22
Figs	55	24
Grapes	100	60
Kiwi fruit (weighed with skin)	75	32
Melon (weighed with skin)	40	6
Nectarines (weighed with skin)	150	54
Oranges (weighed with skin)	200	52
Peaches (weighed with stone)	150	45
Pear	150	50
Pineapple	80	33
Plums (weighed with stone)	70	24
Raspberries	60	15
Satsumas (weighed with skin)	87	23
Strawberries	100	27
Watermelon (flesh only)	200	62
NUTS & SEEDS		
Almonds	15	91
Brazil nuts	10	68
Cashew nuts	10	57
Cashew nuts (roasted and salted)	25	153
Hazelnuts	10	65
Mixed nuts	40	232
Mixed nuts and raisins	40	192
Peanuts (plain)	13	73
Pine nuts	5	34
Pistachio nuts (roasted and salted)	66	218
Pumpkin seeds	16	91
Sunflower seeds	16	93
Walnuts	20	138
VEGETABLES (raw, prepared, unless stated otherwise)		
Beans		
Broad	120	71
French	90	20
Runner	90	20
Beetroot	40	14
Broccoli	85	28

Food	Average portion (g)	Calories
Brussels sprouts	90	38
Cabbage	90	23
Carrots	60	21
Cauliflower	90	31
Celery	30	2
Chilli peppers	10	3
Courgettes	90	17
Cucumber	100	11
Leeks	75	16
Lettuce	80	13
Mushrooms	80	10
Onions	150	54
Parsnips	65	43
Peas	70	55
Peppers	160	51
Potatoes		
New (boiled)	175	131
Old (baked with flesh & skin **NO** butter)	180	245
Old (boiled)	175	126
Radishes	48	6
Spinach	90	23
Spring onions	10	4
Swede	130	31
Sweetcorn	60	56
Tomatoes	85	14
CHEESE		
Brie	40	137
Cheddar	40	166
Cheese spread	30	81
Cottage, 4% fat	40	36
Cottage, 2% fat	40	28
Edam	40	136
Emmental	40	153
Feta	50	125
Gouda	40	151
Mozzarella (fresh)	55	141
Mozzarella (grated)	40	103
Parmesan (freshly grated)	20	82
Red Leicester	40	161
Ricotta	55	79
Roquefort	28	105
Soft light	30	47
Soft medium fat	30	60

Calories

Food	Average portion (g)	Calories
EGGS		
Boiled	50	74
Fried	60	107
Poached	50	74
Omelette (plain, 2 eggs)	120	234
Scrambled (no milk, 2 eggs)	100	160
MILK		
Semi-skimmed	146	67
Skimmed	146	48
Whole	146	96
MEAT		
Beef		
Fillet steak (grilled)	168	316
Mince (extra lean, stewed)	140	248
Lamb		
Leg steaks (grilled)	90	178
Loin chops (grilled)	70	149
Mince (extra lean, stewed)	90	187
Pork		
Bacon (back rashers, grilled)	100	287
Fillet of pork (grilled)	120	204
Ham		
Parma	47	105
Premium	56	74
POULTRY		
Chicken	130	192
Breast (skinless, grilled)	90	145
Breast strips (stir-fried)	47	71
Drumsticks (skinned, roasted)	146	257
Leg quarter (skinned, casseroled)	45	81
Thighs (skinless, boneless, casseroled)	100	226
Wings (grilled)		
Turkey	90	140
Breast (skinless, grilled)	90	146
Drumsticks (skinned, roasted)	90	158
Mince (stewed)	90	148
Strips (stir-fried)	90	163
Thighs (diced, skinless, boneless, casseroled)		
FISH & SEAFOOD	10	19
Anchovies (in oil)	40	31
Crab (in brine)	120	125

Food	Average portion (g)	Calories
Haddock (grilled)	150	201
Smoked haddock (poached)	100	113
Hake (grilled)	145	175
Halibut (grilled)	110	169
Halibut (poached)	130	125
Plaice (grilled)	60	59
Prawns (boiled, shelled)	56	80
Salmon (smoked)	40	78
Sardines (grilled)	70	83
Scallops (steamed, shelled)	45	45
Tuna (canned in brine)	45	61
Tuna (raw)		
RICE, PASTA & PULSES (uncooked, unless stated otherwise)	100	353
Bulgar wheat	100	77
Butter beans (canned)	100	103
Butter beans (dried, boiled)	100	87
Cannellini beans (canned)	100	115
Chickpeas (canned)	100	121
Chickpeas (dried, boiled)	100	227
Cous cous	100	118
Lentils (puy-style, canned)	100	105
Lentils (puy-style, dried, boiled)	100	100
Kidney beans (canned)	125	108
Macaroni (boiled)	125	78
Noodles, egg (boiled)		
Rice	125	176
Brown (boiled)	125	82
White (glutinous, boiled)	125	154
White (polished, boiled)	125	130
Spaghetti (boiled)	125	141
Spaghetti (wholemeal, boiled)		
BREAD		
Crumpets	40	83
French baguette	40	109
Muffins (English, white)	68	152
Pitta bread	75	191
Rolls		
Brown	48	113
White (crusty)	50	131
White (soft)	45	114
Wholemeal	48	117
Sliced		
Brown	36	75